Mike

21.11.06

A STIFLED VOICE

Mike Gerrard

Pen Press Publishers Ltd

First published in Great Britain by
Pen Press Publishers Ltd
The Old School
39 Chesham Road
Brighton BN2 1NB

ISBN: 1-905621-61-2
ISBN13: 978-1-905621-61-3

Printed and bound in the UK

A catalogue record of this book is available from
the British Library

Cover design by Jacqueline Abromeit

Farewell To Community Health Councils

"The input of the CHC will be much missed. It has performed an important role in the scrutiny of health services in South Warwickshire. You and your colleagues have ensured that the Primary Care Trust has remained fully aware of the aspirations and requirements of the population we all serve. Our services are more sensitive to need because of the CHC's work. The PCT hopes to maintain the relationships it has developed with CHC members and associates through its public and patient involvement initiative. I hope so too – South Warwickshire cannot afford to lose their experience and expertise, developed through the CHC.

Health services in South Warwickshire will need to continue to develop and modernise... There will be more challenges ahead. I know I speak for many when I say that I hope that the new overview and scrutiny arrangements will incorporate all that has been best about the CHC."

Margaret Pratt, Non-Executive Director,
South Warwickshire Primary Care Trust,
in a letter to Councillor Bill Lowe,
Chairman of South Warwickshire Community Health Council,
3 September 2003

* * *

"I realise this is a difficult time for both CHC staff and members, but in the long run Parliament made the right decision for patients and the public as a whole."

Rosie Winterton MP, Minister of State, Department of Health,
in a farewell letter to CHCs, 21 August 2003

CHAIRMEN OF THE ASSOCIATION OF COMMUNITY HEALTH COUNCILS FOR ENGLAND AND WALES 1977–2003

Gordon Bessey	1977–1979
Rod Griffiths	1979–1981
Merlin Thomas	1981–1982
John Austin-Walker	1982–1984
John Butler	1984–1986
Wyn Pockett	1986–1989
Hywel Wyn Jones	1989–1990
Rita Lewis	1990–1992
Eleanor Young	1992–1995
Jennifer Elliott	1995–1998
Joyce Struthers	1998–2000
Alan Hartley	2000–2003

DIRECTORS OF THE ASSOCIATION

Mike Gerrard	1977–1983
Tony Smythe	1983–1986
Toby Harris	1987–1998
Donna Covey	1998–2001
Peter Walsh	2001–2002
Malcolm Alexander	2003

CHYE CHOO was the senior member of staff, serving from the formation of the Steering Group in 1975 until the dissolution of the Association in 2003.

In 1974, there were 205 Community Health Councils in England. By the time they were abolished in 2003, this number had reduced to 184.

Acknowledgements

This book is the product of a large amount of time spent researching and revisiting the events and personalities it describes, and once completed, preparing it for publication. I started working on it in June 2003, and am writing this acknowledgement more than three years later, in August 2006. The pace of events is such that while this unavoidable time lapse has enabled me to add some interesting new elements to the book, it has also necessitated a number of revisions to ensure that it remains as accurate as possible.

My thanks are due, first to Chye Choo, who put the idea into my head early in 2003 while visiting Kenwood House, and to Rita Lewis, who had already started working on it and with whom I began in collaboration. I am sorry that Rita dropped out early on, and have always hoped that her reason for doing so was not on account of any fault on my part.

I have many people to thank for their part in its completion: above all the MPs and ex-MPs and ministers who answered my letters and telephone calls, and especially those who permitted me to interview them at length. Similar thanks go to the many former colleagues and friends who worked in or were members of CHCs, whose recollections and reflections animated so much of the book. Particular thanks to Mary Marre for her written contributions and for the papers she passed on to me, to Jean Lovell-Davis for her dossier on the theory of user representation; to Jean Robinson for access to her written work on the GMC; to Malcolm Alexander and Peter Walsh, his predecessor as Director of ACHCEW, for original work of their own, and to the elected officers of the association who gave me free use of its files, and great encouragement in what seemed at the time a daunting task. It became immeasurably more difficult after ACHCEW had closed down and its papers had been dispersed or destroyed.

Special thanks are due to Christine Hogg, who not only agreed to be interviewed, but also sent me her original work as a source, read the book and commented chapter by chapter throughout its painful progress. Her advice and corrections were invaluable. Rod Griffiths and Chye Choo were my principal readers. Their observations without exception were to the point, and stimulated new areas for investigation as I made my way through the CHC story.

My technical knowledge leaves a lot to be desired, and I could not have made the book ready for publication without the help of my daughter and son-in-law Michele and John Steele. John's unstinting help on the numerous occasions I have got into difficulty with the computer has been remarkable, and always successful. I have also benefited hugely from the experience of Dick Sharples and the literary advice he has generously given me.

I am indebted to all those named and many more for their advice and encouragement during what has been a long haul. The book has been improved by their contributions and by their attention to factual accuracy and the relative significance of the events described. Any errors remaining or shortcomings in interpretation or balance are entirely my own responsibility.

In conclusion, I should like to thank my publishers, Pen Press Ltd., for providing the means and the expertise to put this book on the market and my wife Heather, for her truly amazing patience over the long-drawn-out process of its gestation. Her ceaseless enthusiasm kept me working and hoping through every stage, and whatever the merit of the book, its publication is as much her achievement as mine.

Introduction

When I sat down to write this book, my thoughts initially turned towards the origins of Community Health Councils (CHCs) in the growing consumer movement of the 1950s and 60s, and as a by-product of some of the long-stay hospital scandals of the same period. I also saw the obvious precedents in the Consumer Councils which the conventions of the day demanded should be established for each of the nationalised industries: a model which must have seemed to be adaptable for the biggest public enterprise of them all. I recalled them as being a new element added at a late stage to the legislation for the reorganisation of the NHS in 1973; how they had to be rushed into existence on the very last day of the year and eventually became a reality under the Labour government which assumed office at the end of February 1974.

You might call this an obvious and unsurprising approach. But as I looked back through the papers and I saw how little consideration appeared to have been given to them up to the time their purpose and functioning was debated in parliament; how ministers seemed to be thinking on their feet and apparently ad-libbing answers to questions from their own supporters as well as from the opposition, and how the story evolved as it went along, I realised that there was more to be taken into account than just the obvious.

Of course it's true that the creation of CHCs for England and Wales – and their counterparts in Scotland and Northern Ireland, the Local Health Councils and District Committees – had much to do with contemporary thinking about the accountability of state-managed monopolies to the public. No less certainly, a reorganisation of the health service which eliminated its long-standing and traditional links with local government and public health, establishing a new managerial hierarchy to run the entire undertaking, upset a large number of public service preconceptions. It's also true that many interests, inside and outside of parliament, wanted to see some form of local accountability in place as a counterweight to the new management monolith. But the miracle to my mind is the way in which a laudable but unpolished idea, stitched into major legislation, but given a non-specific form and only scantily resourced, survived and flourished, and in its own way revolutionised the NHS.

This book is chiefly about community health councils in England, which were summarily abolished in the year 2000, although for administrative reasons, they stayed in place until December 2003. Local Health Councils (LHCs) in Scotland remained in existence until the early part of 2005 before being replaced by one countrywide Health Council, while the Welsh CHCs are still functional at the time of writing. During less than thirty years' lifetime, the CHCs in England generated a nationwide upsurge of good will for the health service, brought a new way of thinking into its processes, and gave the management, the professions, the civil service and the government a great deal to think about, while achieving some quite remarkable successes and throwing up a number of highly distinguished people along the way. By the time they were disbanded, they had become so integral to the operation of the NHS that their abolition without some form of replacement was unthinkable.

So this book is my personal fanfare and valediction for English Community Health Councils: the unloved offspring of two opposing political philosophies, abolished finally for being what their parents had made them. Yet they outlived all the other creations of the 1973 NHS Reorganisation Act. Regional and Area Health Authorities; Family Practitioner Committees, and all the minor paraphernalia of district management, service planning and inter-authority working had been recycled, in some cases several times, long before the so-called "toothless watchdogs". It was the energy, the enterprise, the vision, the foresight, the capability and the commitment of the members and staff of CHCs over those thirty years which kept them alive so long, and which under laid their achievements. What I have written here is my tribute to them.

Contents

Chapter One

The End of the Affair

"This is a package of radical reform. It will enhance and encourage the involvement of citizens in redesigning the health service from the patient's point of view. As a result community health councils will be abolished and funding redirected…"

(The NHS Plan, July 2000)

Just like that. No advance notice, no threats or subtle hints: after more than twenty-five years in the health service and all the contacts and co-operation that had been engineered over the period, just that. I asked Donna Covey, who was Director of the Association of Community Health Councils (ACHCEW) at the time, whether she had any inkling of what was about to happen. She assured me that it was a complete surprise. ACHCEW had been talking with civil servants about ways of reforming and improving CHCs and had a clear understanding that they had a future. A completely new and alarming situation was sprung on her without any prior warning. Moreover, the timing was as inconvenient as it could be. The first action of any organisation confronted with an announcement of this kind must be to gather its key people together and determine how to respond. But this was the end of July – the peak of the holiday season – when many of the leading members and staff of CHCs and their association were away from home and difficult to contact, let alone bring together.

The treatment given to CHCs and to Donna Covey is a classic example of one of the less engaging habits of British governments, which seem consciously to announce their most disruptive decisions at the times when least can be done about them; just before the summer parliamentary recess (as in this case), or on Christmas Eve. Secretary of State for Health, Alan Milburn, courageously delegated the duty of notifying Donna in person to Parliamentary Under Secretary Gisela Stuart.

One of the immediate consequences was to precipitate a huge volume of work for ACHCEW and community health councils around the country, the pace of which scarcely faltered over the following two years. An intensive and highly effective anti-abolition campaign was set up, supported by many back-bench MPs; by an astonishing number of influential NHS managers and professionals; by almost all the national voluntary organisations in the health and community care sector; by numerous prominent people; and given publicity (and often support) in local and national newspapers and other communications media.

David Spilsbury of South Birmingham CHC described the national response to this campaign as "unexpected and heart-warming ... every voluntary and public body which had had any direct contact with CHCs leapt to their defence." The case for the retention, adaptation, modernisation or possibly even the 'rebranding' of CHCs was argued closely and persuasively in letters to ministers and the press by many groups and individuals who did not wish to see their input and accumulated experience lost to the NHS, which they believed would be impoverished as a result. Although it was generally recognised that the odds were unfavourable: that the government had made its intentions totally clear, and that in the last resort, parliament had the absolute right to abolish any institution it had itself created, the co-ordination between individual councils and their association was impressive, and the lobby of parliament (for the report stage of the Health and Social Care Bill) on 14th February 2001 particularly secured extensive national media coverage.

Originally lined up for abolition in 2002, CHCs received more than one stay of execution. Eventually, on 31 January 2003, junior minister David Lammy wrote to all concerned to confirm 1 September that year as the firm shutdown date. Even this was later deferred to 1 December 2003, but this time there was no way out, and although the new arrangements for patient and public involvement were less than fully in place, the axe was allowed to fall. By one of those ironies that frequently attend political decisions, this ensured that CHCs nonetheless outlived the Secretary of State Alan Milburn, who resigned 'for family reasons' in June that year.

It had taken the government three years and four months to put its decision into effect, and throughout that time the normal work of CHCs continued. Meetings and other interactions with NHS Hospital and Primary Care Trusts remained on the agenda, as did all the standard services to the public, including personal advice and consultation on service changes proposed by the local health services.

In addition to all this, the staff of the councils found themselves helping fledgling patients' forums (who were to take over from them) with information and training, and preparing the way for Patient Advisory and Liaison Services (PALS) and the Independent Complaints Advisory Service (ICAS) about to come into being locally.

At a time when many of them would have been worrying about their own future, the demands on them must have been quite harrowing. It is greatly to their credit that over such an extended period, with the end increasingly inevitable and drawing closer, in the majority of cases they put their backs, first, into the business of campaigning, and later into the handover to their successors, while still carrying on the core business of the CHC to the best of their ability, knowing there was no future in what they were doing. Like beaten sportsmen, they played mainly for their pride, and having done their best, they could hold their heads up high.

In preparing this book, I met, spoke to and exchanged letters with a large number of people who had worked in CHCs, either as members or as staff. Almost all of them are proud of what CHCs – and especially their own CHC – had achieved. Summing up her feelings about the anti-abolition campaign and what it achieved, Donna Covey told me "I am very proud of what CHCs and ACHCEW achieved, because it's had a lasting impact. Nobody would have expected us to have achieved so much... I'm also very proud that we held the line... Holding together a coalition of people with really different interests in a way that could effect change made me really proud (of them)".

Expressing their emotions in terms of pride is a mark of the commitment shown by people all over the country who worked in and guided the work of their councils. Those who take pride in their work, whatever their trade or profession, will reflect on it with pride. Day to day they work diligently and with greater enthusiasm than those who are bored or disgruntled, and they work for positive reasons. Their work thus has a clearer purpose, and consequently a superior final product. To me it is a truly significant part of the story of CHCs: that those most closely involved believed in what they were doing and put their hearts, their energy and their pride into their work.

Many CHC staff and members were highly gifted people, and made a great political or intellectual contribution to the cause. Others contributed as much through their enthusiasm or common sense. It is not necessary to be highly talented or inspired (although it may be a help). Belief is the essential component, and among CHC people there was a great deal of belief in the NHS and the contribution they were making towards its betterment.

It is worth recording at this point that pride was not the only emotional response from people with CHC backgrounds. There was a lot of disappointment, incomprehension and anger expressed, from a surprising variety of sources. Much regret was felt by former politicians and mixed feelings were admitted by sitting MPs and others who felt obliged to nod their heads in the direction of the changes as the will of parliament, but were reluctant to be associated personally with the government's decision. This really was one of the most bizarre, unnecessary and self-defeating ministerial decisions imaginable, as any examination of it will demonstrate.

Firstly, it was unnecessary, because nowhere has it ever been claimed that CHCs were so incompetent, unpopular or hidebound that they could not have been reformed or adapted to do the work of one or more components of the proposed new structure. As I shall go on to make clear, they had been attempting to 'modernise' themselves in different ways over the previous ten years, and were neither hostile to change of a positive kind nor averse to a division of labour that might lead to new partnerships and a greater range of representational services for users of the NHS. The support that Donna Covey's campaign attracted made it clear that there was no question of unpopularity or lack of public confidence. Abolition at that stage was obviously not a necessity.

It was also self-defeating and somehow rather sad, because in peremptorily axing CHCs, Alan Milburn made it clear how little the government valued the hard work and good will invested in the health service over the previous twenty-five years by perhaps as many thousands of CHC members and staff. Worse still, given that a fair proportion of them might originally have been well-disposed to Labour, his decision would undoubtedly have soured their attitudes towards his party. Furthermore, it must have embarrassed the Department of Health, which was unable to put the new arrangements in place in anything like the timescale envisaged in the Secretary of State's NHS Plan.

Finally, by his personal decision, he deprived every district and NHS trust in the country at a stroke of the accumulated experience, memory and records of their local CHC and its association. All these considerations suggest a ministerial blunder of monumental ineptitude.

Recognising therefore that the abolition of CHCs was both unnecessary and counter-productive; that politically it could only harm the government, and that it was foisted on an unsuspecting country without warning, never having been put to or debated in parliament, the term 'bizarre' does seem unquestionably apt. When the disruption it caused over the ensuing three years and the relative cost of the new patient and public involvement framework is added to the equation, it is approaching unbelievable that Alan Milburn is still a figure of some consequence in government circles. Fortunately for him and for the nation the issue on this occasion was not one of major economic or strategic significance.

The rationale for the proposals in the NHS Plan is set out in paragraph 10.23:

> "In 1974, the then Government tried to give greater prominence to the views of patients by creating CHCs. They attempted to combine three distinct functions: supporting individual patients and complainants; monitoring local hospital and community (but not primary care) services; and providing a citizen's perspective on service changes. It is time to modernise, deepen and broaden the way that patient views are represented within the NHS."

It is easy to read this as an effort at rationalising the decision to abolish CHCs which follows. But the substantive issue was not fought on modernisation, nor on the depth or breadth of patient representation. It was fought on the same ground as in the early days: that community health councils (being unelected) were unrepresentative and undemocratic; and more importantly, that their performance was highly variable.

Professor Rudolf Klein, who although he found them a fascinating and sometimes remunerative source of study in the 1970s was never an enthusiast for CHCs, and his colleague Janet Lewis made these points in their wide-ranging 1976 study "The Politics of Consumer Representation". They noted the age, gender, class, experience and political skews intrinsic to the methods of appointing CHC members, and questioned their democratic credentials, whether indirectly elected as members of local authorities ("a universal credit card which allows him/her to represent the community in a totally different capacity") or otherwise appointed ("it is the lack of responsibility to any constituency that vitiates the arrangements for consumer representation").

With regard to performance, they felt confident enough to say: "CHCs inevitably vary in their attitudes and in their degree of activity: some are thrusters, a few are sleepers. It cannot be taken for granted that they will necessarily be most effective in producing information about consumer views in those districts where the deficiencies in the NHS are most urgent." They even went so far as to anticipate and legitimise what Labour's NHS Plan so many years later turned into reality: "this is not to say that CHCs should be considered sacrosanct or inviolable if... Government were to decide to change the... structure of the NHS for other reasons. In a changing NHS, there would also be scope for changes in the way the consumer interest is represented."

Much of the criticism levelled at community health councils in their early days centred around arguments of this kind, and at the time of "Patients First" (1980–81) as we shall see later, the real issues were clouded by rhetoric of a similar nature. The arguments about the representative and democratic standing of CHCs tended to subside and to become less important once councils and their association had begun to make their mark and to be admitted to areas of health service management and regulation previously reserved for managers, professionals and civil servants. But they never completely vanished, for their echo could at times be detected throughout the CHC era. Quite late in the day Dr Mikko Vienonen of the World Health Organisation, guest speaker at the ACHCEW conference at Eastbourne in 1999, presenting a SWOT analysis (Strengths, Weaknesses, Opportunities and Threats) for CHCs, drew attention to the "democratic deficit". This expression was also much used in support of Alan Milburn's argument, and was heard many times during the wrangling over abolition between 2000 and 2002. But for the most part, it was something of a passenger while CHCs matured, and faced different challenges in the later 1980s and 1990s.

The predominant issue throughout this period was the establishment of performance standards for community health councils. My reading of ACHCEW and CHC papers between 1989 and 1998 identifies this persistent theme, emanating not only from external sources, but equally from among CHCs, regional associations of CHCs, and advocates for CHCs, such as Christine Hogg.[*] In fact, there is a sense in which the search for performance standards is the *leitmotiv* of Toby Harris's time as Director of ACHCEW. In my day the key objective was to get CHCs accepted as a valuable adjunct to the NHS structure, and to give them the information and support to help them operate confidently and effectively. For Toby, CHC performance issues were under the microscope, and the pressure was coming from both sides.

---

[*] Christine Hogg was the original secretary of the CHC for what was known as the South district of Kensington, Chelsea and Westminster Area Health Authority, in West London. After some years as CHC secretary, she moved into the academic arena, publishing many books and articles on consumer involvement in public services. A notable part of her work was research papers written for CHCs and ACHCEW. Christine is a seminal figure in the history of CHCs, and I shall have a great deal more to say about her and her work in the course of this book.

Already in 1989, Christine Hogg was giving CHCs what turned out to be their half-time pep talk. In a paper entitled "Representing the Consumer – Community Health Councils Fifteen Years On", the first substantive topic she addressed was Evaluating the Performance of CHCs. Six months later, after the November 1989 Department of Health internal paper on the Role of CHCs had been published, she was sufficiently sure of her ground to write: "It is generally accepted that community health councils need to be reformed... standards and operational policies... will be developed."

It appears that the development of these standards was rather more difficult than she anticipated, since the following ten years, which included:

(i)   the only time a minister ever addressed the standing committee of ACHCEW (Stephen Dorrell, then Parliamentary Secretary for Health), which was followed by some quite positive instructions to health service managers on dealing with CHCs;

(ii) the abolition of regional health authorities (the establishing bodies for CHCs) and the consequential new management arrangements put into effect;

(iii) the consultants' report "Resourcing and Performance Management in CHCs" (the Insight report), and

(iv) a change of government,

while clearly eventful, still found Toby in August 1998 corresponding with the Health Quality Service at the King's Fund on the latest set of proposals for a performance evaluation framework for CHCs.

Toby himself did not seem to attach so much weight as I to the volume of his work which was concerned with the setting of performance standards. We discussed it one summer evening in 2003 on the terrace of the House of Lords, with a party going on in one of the riverside rooms nearby, heavy rush-hour traffic on the embankment, and much summertime activity on the river. In this agreeable, if somewhat noisy setting, Toby was free to reflect on my question, and told me that he had spent a lot of time on it, but that the bulk of his work involved the promotion of issues surrounding the health service.

He conceded that much of the sound and fury of his years in office was to do with the standing of community health councils and the continuing internal debate surrounding it: he added that systems of self-assessment had been initiated and developed by CHCs and that there was "quite a fair degree of peer review" among CHCs concerned with performance issues. He went on to say that ACHCEW was at the same time in dialogue with the regional offices of the NHS, aimed at encouraging them to adopt performance management criteria consistent with those developed by CHCs themselves. All this was beneficial, in his opinion, because CHCs seemed to be put under heavy ministerial scrutiny about every two to three years, and had there not been a willingness among them to collaborate in the business of performance review, "the end would have come a lot earlier".

If it had been difficult to arrive at performance standards for CHCs themselves, there was one important area in which they were achieved. A code of conduct for the members of CHCs was agreed and produced in the mid-1990s; published by the DoH and the NHS Executive, and circulated to all CHC members. It clearly underwent a number of changes in its lifetime, since a revised edition was published in July 1999. This code of conduct is of particular interest to me, since my recollection of CHC members is that they had no wish to be squeezed into a mould any more than they would tolerate their councils being made to behave in a uniform way. They must have become more amenable as time passed: either that, or they were subjected to greater pressure than my generation dared apply. Early in 2002 I had the testing experience of being asked to sit on a NHS Appeals Panel in respect of a complaint made (unusually) against a CHC by a member of the public. The code of conduct was helpful in reaching what I believe was a fair conclusion.

One thing is certain, and that is that the pressure for standard setting and performance review did not fall uniquely on community health councils. The managerial leanings of the Conservative government at the time were directed firmly at all aspects of the public service, and were expressed not only in privatisations, but equally in the focus on public and private partnerships; "balance sheet" evaluation of public sector activity of all kinds, and the application of new accountabilities to local authorities, voluntary organisations and other public representative bodies. CHCs could not possibly escape this kind of attention, and they were known to vary in their attitudes and methods of working; their relations with health service management, and their political position.

There is nothing odd about this: it applies to a greater or less degree to representative bodies in all areas, including those of private businesses, and members of parliament. But with CHCs it seemed to be a particular sore point, and always had. In 1974, they were perceived as a threat by many health authorities and professionals. Their patient representative function was labelled as 'power without responsibility' and they were accused of stridency, superficiality or political motivation. Critics even then were careful to point out that this did not apply to CHCs in general: *some, but not all* were thoughtful and responsible. The variable quality argument was on the move.

I did not subscribe to this point of view, because as I saw it, the main purpose at the time was to establish a patient-centred bridgehead at the gates of the NHS. Many NHS staff and managers were uncertain about the changes brought about by the health service reorganisation, and the legislation itself made different approaches possible. Since no two health districts were identical, the problems facing CHC members as they took office were different in every case, requiring a tailor-made local response strategy. This was bound to involve diverse tactical approaches, which councils would adopt according to their own judgment. Experience would indicate where and in which circumstances these were most likely to be effective.

Lady Mary Marre, who was one of the ministerial advisers on CHCs at the time they took up their duties, had this to say on the variability question: "It would have been extraordinary if there had *not* been considerable variation of performance among the various CHCs. There was no independent body assessing such performance. In any locally based organisation the performance will vary according to the skills and commitment of the members and the staff appointed to assist them. Many CHCs were fortunate [and attracted excellent staff] who, under difficulties, provided good services." These she enumerated as building contact networks; arranging meetings and visits; producing reports and keeping records. She might also have included provision of advice and information – to members and to the public alike.

The quality argument was at all times a tactical weapon for those organisations or individuals who were hostile to community health councils altogether, or to one CHC in particular. Toby Harris felt that the decision to abolish CHCs was "very personal" to Alan Milburn who, he explained, had had a difficult relationship with Darlington – "quite a good" CHC as he saw it (Mr Milburn himself gave me a rather different reason).

For a more colourful illustration of this point, I shall turn to an earlier Secretary of State, Patrick (now Lord) Jenkin. He first became shadow Minister in 1975, and began to make contact "with a large number of leading doctors, both officially through the BMA, and also in other groups". He also established an "extremely good link" with managers, through the Director of the Westminster Hospital. They used to meet once a fortnight for discussions. What emerged from these meetings was "their total hostility to what they called the 'little communes'... which they felt were agents of subversion... continuing to fight the class war".

To anyone who was associated with CHCs at that time, this language is quite incredible, as indeed is the thought that people expressing views of this kind should have had the ear of a Secretary of State in waiting. And there is more to it than that. Lord Jenkin told me that the process was one of learning and gradually clarifying policies: "We had the report of the Royal Commission to work on, but a great deal of my policy had emerged from these discussions with the consultants and the administrators." I once spent a Saturday at a meeting of the Conservative Medical Society while they debated Sir Douglas Black's report "Inequalities in Health". I heard for myself the terms in which they described Sir Douglas, who also was present, and later continued lustily savaging each other from each side of the argument. So I will believe anything, especially from so distinguished an informant.

It does not pay to underrate either the virulence or the influence of your opponents, and there is no doubt that the variable quality argument was part of a consistent attack on CHCs, dusted off each time one of Toby Harris's three year cycles came round. Despite its essentially anecdotal or impressionistic nature, it contains a fatal grain of truth and can be persuasively used by managers, professionals, civil servants or politicians, as it was whenever the future of CHCs came under the spotlight. The need to refute it was one reason why ACHCEW and CHCs in the field felt obliged to establish acceptable minimum standards for CHC performance.

I have dealt with these questions at length because they were some of the more intractable problems that bedevilled the life of community health councils during the countdown to 1st May 1997, and could not be shaken off. The election of a new government must therefore have seemed very welcome to many of them, not for party political reasons, but for the same reasons that led to the national political landslide that day. At last it seemed that there might be room for some new ideas; a more adventurous approach to government coming in on the back of a mission to overhaul and modernise the country's institutions and working practices. Perhaps CHCs could at last come into their own and begin to play a serious part in educating the public and empowering them to get the best out of the NHS.

In the policy paper on health presented to its annual conference in 1995, Labour had promised to give patients greater representation in NHS management: "Health authorities and hospital boards will not be stuffed full of party political placemen, but will be openly selected and broadly based to reflect the communities they serve". The party undertook to transform CHCs ("the neglected voice of the patient") into Local Health Advocates with new powers to raise standards in hospitals and in general practice, and to provide more information to patients. In this capacity, they would monitor local authority community care services as well as every aspect of the health service. Besides having a voice at health authority meetings, they were to scrutinise the strategic plan of the health authority to make sure that patients' views would be taken into account. But there were some things they had not realised about New Labour.

The first signs were good. Frank Dobson, who when needed had been a useful ally to CHCs and was well known and liked among CHC members and staff, particularly in London, was appointed Secretary of State for Health, and accepted an invitation to address the Bournemouth conference of ACHCEW in 1997. In his speech he laid stress, as everyone had expected, on the need for CHCs to be reformed and the promise of an enhanced role as a result. His audience had been in the throes of searching for ways to modernise themselves for much of the preceding ten years, and were therefore not dismayed by what they heard.

Frank Dobson however was not completely uncritical of CHCs. I asked him for his assessment, and he outlined his perception of CHCs in general as a spectrum, with a few supine councils at one extreme and a small number of manic councils at the other. In between lay the councils business could be done with and "by and large, they did a fairly good job". He was prepared to accept that similar judgment might be passed on local authorities, health authorities or even MPs, but felt it applied with particular relevance to CHCs.

Questioned on their representative function, he commented that "they've been reasonably professional, at least the ones in my area; the ones I've dealt with." He could see the possibility of extending CHC responsibilities in their representative role, but with the reservation that "they were always a little between the devil and the deep, in that they didn't have democratic legitimacy and they weren't part of the system either." To be fair to CHCs, he made the point that in his view, under the new NHS Trust and PCT regime, there would be an organised information feed into the system that hadn't existed previously, resulting in a closer reflection of local needs in their policies and priorities. The representational function in the redress of grievances was the missing bit which CHCs did well.

All in all, Frank Dobson's estimate of CHCs gives them at best a C+ to B- rating, with the best mark given to the handling of complaints. Asked to elaborate on the variable quality proposition, he acknowledged that local authorities have the same problem. They would have had the democratic legitimacy, but there was no reason to suppose that they would have dealt with redress of grievances very well. Direct election to CHCs, he conceded, would not necessarily produce the right sort of people: "I'm in favour of elected bodies, but I'm not very keen on the idea of electing bodies for specific tasks." He confirmed to me that had he been Secretary of State at the time of the NHS Plan, CHCs would have remained as a component of the elaborated patient and public involvement structure, though there would have been some functional changes, and whether they would have remained permanently was an open question.

In conclusion, he expressed the opinion that the main legacy CHCs had left to the health service was the idea of local lay involvement in redress of grievances. He also believed that CHCs had had a role in making the professions more open to involving patients in their own health care and listening to their views. He acknowledged the part internal changes in the professions had played over the past twenty years, but was equally sure that CHCs had been a contributory factor.

Frank Dobson's views are important, because he was seen as a friendly Secretary of State, and because had it not been for the Ken Livingstone affair and his propulsion out of the cabinet to stand for Labour in the first London mayoral election in 2000, CHCs might still be in action today. It is salutary to note that even he did not rate them too highly, other than in the ICAS role, and was conditional in the prognosis he would have given them had he remained in office.

There were other aspects to the new government that might have raised alarm if their implications had been realised. Government in this country during the twentieth century (with the possible exception of the Labour administration of 1945–51) was largely pragmatic, dealing with policy questions on an empirical basis, and apart from election campaigns, leaving the philosophical issues to the theorists. The election in 1979 changed all that, and Margaret

Thatcher, as Prime Minister, introduced a brand of conviction government, which, while anathema to some politicians, was exciting and venturesome in the eyes of much of the population.

Mrs Thatcher prospered for ten years, and in many ways changed the face of British politics, jettisoning most of the "old school" Tories along the way, and altering values, especially with regard to public services and industrial relations, out of all recognition. From the Falklands war, through the Miners' strike, to the first major privatisations, her government revolutionised the institutions of the country and left the other main political parties stranded in its wake.

Labour and the Liberals were shaken to the roots, in Labour's case through the demolition of its territory and the defection of many activists and academics to the newly-formed SDP with disastrous electoral consequences; and in the Liberals', through having to face up to their political irrelevance and the need to combine with the SDP in the hope of creating a working alternative to the Thatcher government. Eventually, both parties were to revive; the Labour Party re-launching itself as New Labour and the resurgent Liberals under Paddy Ashdown absorbing the SDP and in turn re-branding themselves as Liberal Democrats.

Any politician entering parliament between 1979 and 1992 would have seen what was taking place and recognised the fundamental change the country had undergone. The younger ones would have had little memory of how government had previously been organised, and over a period of up to eighteen years would have observed the success of conviction politics before its corruption in the early 1990s, and drawn their own conclusions. Tony Blair became an MP in 1983, and many of his associates entered parliament at the same time, or in 1987 or 1992. By 1997 they had evolved their own form of conviction government, and had it ready to put into practice.

New Labour is a conviction government, which accepts the revolution of the 1980s and is prepared to work to the new political rules laid down by Mrs Thatcher (Mr Blair makes no secret of his admiration of Margaret Thatcher as a political leader). The traditional commitment to public ownership in industry, power, transport and communications has gone, and has been replaced by a commitment to modernisation of public services and administration. A number of old-style socialists have been jettisoned along the way. This new political force was what community health council members and staff were waking up to on 2nd May 1997.

Conviction: modernisation; the two key elements of New Labour; both vital to the story from this point onwards. The essence of conviction government is that it is utterly certain of what it proposes, and does not tolerate any alternative. It does not allow gradations of opinion: the line must be followed. The practicalities of party politics dictate in favour of coalitions, and a government has to accept the sometimes lukewarm support of some of its adherents. One great advantage the conviction governments of the past twenty-five years have enjoyed is a large parliamentary majority, which makes it possible, first, substantially to ignore the dissentients, and second, to proceed without regard for their views, in the reasonable certainty of success (this, of course, may be changing in the wake of the 2005 election). The only course for objectors has been to put up with what is done in their name, or to move elsewhere. In the latter case, they are easily replaced. There is always someone willing enough to fill the gap.

Modernisation rides hand in hand with conviction, in that where conviction provides the certainty, the modernisation drive turns certainty into action, and the action is buttressed by the conviction which underlies it. Modernisation in practice is accompanied by a diminution in tolerance. Nothing that departs from the policies and courses of action advocated is acceptable; alternative proposals are taken to be inferior or even hostile to the core objectives, and everyone concerned is whipped in to conform. The message is clear and undiluted; all those involved can stay "on message" without difficulty, but it is also narrow and unaccommodating.

Furthermore, modernisation in practice is concerned first and foremost with the way its progress is perceived rather than the underlying reality of what is taking place. There are obvious advantages where reality and perceptions coincide, but where there is a variation, everything is still all right, provided that the perception remains favourable. Modernisation is defensive, because it attempts to exclude all non-conforming elements and present a smooth, uniform surface. It will go to great lengths to ensure that this is achieved. At the same time it is assertive (and sometimes aggressively so) in order to achieve its objectives and quell any alternative. This aspect is useful in dealing with dissent.

I am conscious that many of the facets of government and policy formation described above will be attractive to any political organisation. Clear, unequivocal statements are worth their weight in gold, and consistent presentation creates public confidence. A strong message is impressive, and internal discipline is invaluable in boosting popularity. But these features should be the product of serious debate within the organisation and a search for genuine solutions to perceived problems or unfulfilled needs, carried out in a spirit of co-operation and readiness to see alternative points of view. What they have too often appeared to be in this country in recent years is more a determination that the leadership should have its way at any price.

Community health councils prepared themselves to work with the new government, and the situation appeared to be "business as usual". In the background, ministers and civil servants were working on the new shape of the health service. NHS hospital trusts remained in place, but fundholding GPs became a thing of the past, and area-based primary care groups were set up to prepare the way for the primary care trusts which were shortly to come into existence. The Private Finance Initiative (PFI) stayed firmly in position as a means of raising the vast capital sums required for building the new generation of hospitals the government had promised would be created without increasing the amount of tax levied by its predecessor. At the same time, the concept of Foundation Hospitals was being solidified for presentation to parliament, the NHS and the country.

ACHCEW continued to search for a workable system of performance measurements for CHCs, and an enterprising group of Chief Officers led by Barrie Taylor (South West Hertfordshire CHC) and Beryl Furr (Southend CHC) embarked on talks with the European Office of the World Health Organisation in Copenhagen concerning user involvement in health services in countries both inside and outside the European Union. This project was to lead to some interesting contacts in the EU, the former Eastern Bloc countries and Israel, and Dr Vienonen's visit to Eastbourne in 1999.

A review of the agendas and minutes of ACHCEW and of South Warwickshire CHC during this period suggests nothing out of the ordinary, and it must be concluded that there was no obvious sign of what was shortly to explode on their world. Donna Covey said the decision to abolish CHCs was sprung on her as a complete surprise. Nothing I have uncovered does anything to suggest that it was less than a complete surprise to everyone concerned – other than Secretary of State Alan Milburn, and possibly a very small number of his top-level colleagues and confidants.

It was to be expected that community health councils would have some powerful voices raised on their account within parliament itself, given the number of former CHC members and staff sitting on the benches of both houses; notably among the ranks of Labour MPs. One of the biggest disappointments of the "fightback" period was that the voices raised in the event did nothing to influence the minds or the actions of the Secretary of State or the government.

One prominent parliamentary ally of community health councils was the Select Committee on Health. Chaired by David Hinchcliffe, Labour MP for Wakefield until May 2005, the select committee at the time was made up of eleven members with a particular interest and aptitude for health issues. Membership was drawn from the three principal parties in the House of Commons, together with the Independent MP for Wyre Forest (Kidderminster), Dr Richard Taylor. One other member was also a doctor.

Over the years, the select committee had taken evidence from individual CHCs, groups of CHCs and ACHCEW, which it had in general found constructive and useful, and had left a favourable impression. Taking account of David Hinchcliffe's known good will towards CHCs, and the presence of John Austin, Labour MP for Erith and Thamesmead and a former Chair of ACHCEW on the Select Committee, it would have seemed that its influence might have been something of a protective shield for them.

Yet neither Mr Hinchcliffe nor Mr Austin had any idea of what the Secretary of State had in mind for CHCs before their abolition was announced. In common with many public and professional bodies, the select committee reaffirmed its support for them, but after the event, when Mr Milburn's decision had been published, and unlike a number of other proposals in the NHS Plan, this one was not for withdrawal.

I asked David Hinchcliffe whether his committee shared the view of ministers that CHCs were unacceptably variable in performance, and that their functions were ill-defined. He agreed that there was some point to both arguments, but that they cut both ways; for example, "some CHCs have been really effective and [yet attracted criticism because they] upset health authorities in the process, while others have [earned praise, having] been party to, or consented to some

31

disgraceful health authority decisions". With reference to their representational role, Mr Hinchcliffe told me "The ones I have been in contact with did it pretty well. They had the courage to uncover some horrific situations. In my experience, they acted responsibly in taking on the areas of work in which they engaged."

Asked if in his opinion CHCs had failed to keep pace with changes in the NHS and public attitudes towards it, he replied quite simply: "I don't think anyone can keep pace with the rate of recent change in the NHS." He added that to some degree they had been the victims of inadequate legislation. The Select Committee (in tune with Frank Dobson on this point) had recommended a legislative extension to their remit to take in primary care and the patient advocacy function. Self-evidently, the government never acted on this recommendation.

David Hinchcliffe did not accept the argument put forward by former Conservative ministers that CHCs were something of a "thorn in the flesh", or that his committee's views had been discounted by the government. His reaction to this suggestion was "No. I don't think the government have gone that far. I haven't been able to fathom out why they made the ill-thought out decision they took," adding "In my opinion the changes were not properly thought through, and a large number of hard-working people have suffered as a result."

John Austin was very warm, and equally indignant at the treatment given to CHCs. John had stood up for them vigorously in the Select Committee, and he gave me his opinion on their effectiveness:

"I thought they were quite unique in their ability to engage the public in scrutiny of a public service. I think that the whole concept of [presenting the] patient or consumer interest without involvement in the management was very interesting and pioneering, and I believe it worked very well.

"All the criticism of CHCs was that they weren't perfect, and they were inconsistent. I don't think anyone has denied, including the Secretary of State, that the best CHCs did a very useful job and performed very well. The only criticism was that they were a mixed bag. But so too are local authorities; so too are education authorities; members of parliament, local councillors, and so on. But you don't abolish them. You ask what it is that the good ones are doing, how to bring the others up to that level.

One of the criticisms of CHCs was that they weren't very good at dealing with complaints or patient advocacy. But they weren't even set up for that – they did it because there was a vacuum; there was no one else to do it. The best CHCs were good patient advocates without the resources, without the structure, without the legislation.

"They [CHCs] were a very interesting experiment in consumer participation in scrutiny of a monopoly [state] provider. They involved the community, they involved the democratically elected local authority, their balance was maintained to ensure that all interests were there by the nomination process. They were exciting, they were revolutionary, they were innovative, and by and large, I think they did a very good job.

"To abolish something such as CHCs without any clear idea as to what would replace it seems to me to be an act of absolute folly."

* * *

There is however a theory, said to have been aired in *The Observer* some while ago, that places the real responsibility for the abolition of CHCs somewhat higher than Alan Milburn. I don't know if there is any truth in it, but it is offered as a little light relief in an otherwise gloomy tale.

The story goes that 10 Downing Street was looking at public representation in the NHS, and Tony Blair took the view that the health service should have the glossy appearance of a modern commercial corporation, which would necessitate having a proper customer service department. The idea of a Patient Advisory and Liaison Service had already been mooted by the NHS Confederation and others, and had some attraction for the Prime Minister. "That's what I want," said Tony to his staff, and later to Alan Milburn, who at the time was Secretary of State, and was instructed to go away and organise it.

This caused some problems, since the public already had representation in the health service through community health councils. CHCs had a number of public interest functions, but were not in any sense PR bodies. The Department of Health had to find a way of setting up the PALS in accordance with the Prime Minister's wishes while keeping all the other functions running. The solution found was to create Patients' Forums (to handle the monitoring function); an Independent Complaints Advisory Service (to deal with dissatisfaction issues), and to enlist the Overview and Scrutiny committees of local authorities (to provide a politico-operational oversight and rectify the absence of any democratically elected element in the total framework). A new quango with the title "Commission for Patient and Public Involvement in Health" was also established, with the intention of giving a rational and purposeful appearance to this heavyweight structure. When priced, the complete "customer service" facility was found to cost the taxpayer several times as much as CHCs.

It has taken several years to get the new bodies into working order, and even now there is some doubt as to whether they can be described as "fully operational". This has provoked much criticism over the past five years, not least in the earlier days from community health councils, whose abolition had to be postponed on more than one occasion to keep a working structure in place. When they were finally disbanded, their replacement system was neither complete nor ready to go. A junior minister was saddled with responsibility for this fiasco, and transferred into obscurity.

All this may have taken place because Tony Blair thought the NHS should have a customer service department, but hadn't thought it through.

I was never able to verify the story with *The Observer*, and the journalist said to have been instrumental in its publication no longer works there.

Chapter Two

Mounting The Health Guard

"The task now is to develop the CHCs into a powerful forum where consumer views can influence the NHS and where local participation in the running of the NHS can become a reality."

(Democracy in the National Health Service, May 1974)

In their early days (1974 to 1980) community health councils devoted much of their time and ingenuity to trying to make their name and activities known to the public. The Department of Health and Social Security (DHSS) had done a certain amount to give them a sense of belonging, by engaging academics at the King's Fund in London, the Nuffield Centre for Health Service Studies in Leeds and Manchester University to run introductory seminars for members and 'basic training' courses for secretaries (as the chief officers of CHCs were then designated), but had not established any budget for promoting the name or notion of CHCs, for example by television advertising.

The Regional Health Authorities were each given budgets for setting up CHCs in their territory, and put a small amount of money into training, including familiarisation with the NHS. Having recently been completely restructured, the new management of the health service was unfamiliar to almost everyone involved, so this was probably quite useful to a wider audience than just the CHCs.

But while these efforts served to bring CHC members and secretaries into contact with their counterparts from other councils and to give those who needed it a rudimentary knowledge of the NHS, and thus were valuable in their own way, they did little to put the words COMMUNITY HEALTH COUNCIL on the lips of the public, or give them any meaning to the man or woman in the street. That part of the job was left to the CHC in each locality to do on its own account.

CHCs all over England and Wales approached this task in broadly similar ways. None of them had a very lavish budget, so they were forced to look for free publicity, or the cheapest they could find. They were a novelty among the battery of official bodies to be found in every town and city, and this had its advantages. Advance warning of their arrival had been given to the mainstream local press and contact with local reporters was easy. Interviews could be given; meetings and issues trailed, and with a review of the ground they hoped to cover in the early months, two or three weeks' press coverage could be guaranteed.

An introductory deal might be negotiated for advertising space enabling more space to be taken more often for the same price, and there might be additional space on the feature pages for a profile of the chairman, the secretary, and a 'prominent person' who was a member, supporter or even a critic of the CHC. While this intensity of coverage couldn't go on indefinitely, it would be a good start, and it had to be backed up by something more permanent: usually a range of posters and leaflets.

Those explaining what the CHC was about; where and when it met, and who the contacts were, would be for display in council offices (courtesy of the councillor members of the CHC), advice and community centres, libraries, post offices and shops.

Similar display in NHS premises would have to be negotiated with the Area Health Authority. If agreed, they could be put up in hospitals (main notice boards, outpatients, other departments and clinics and so on), health centres, community clinics and offices, but there was no guarantee

37

that they would be agreed, and if they were, that they would be displayed everywhere the CHC had requested. At that time, managers in the NHS were not accustomed to the intrusion of posters (other than the League of Friends) and they found it hard to equate the CHC with *them*. The novelty of posters disturbed them, and they were extremely sensitive to anything that could be remotely construed as criticism or possibly conducive to it.

GPs could be as bad, and their status as independent contractors at first made it difficult in some instances even to deal with them. The GPs in a health centre could overrule a decision of the district administrator, and where they referred the CHC to the Family Practitioner Committee for a decision, an endless negotiation could ensue. But right from the start some doctors agreed to accept CHC posters, and in many health districts co-operation with the local GPs improved year by year.

Handbills were used to advertise meetings and other events. Typically, they could be handed out to shoppers coming out of a supermarket, distributed to commuters at the railway station, or given in bulk to voluntary groups for delivery to their members.

These are fairly obvious lines of approach with a small advertising budget, and CHCs in general followed them. Local radio followed in the wake of the local press and some CHCs looked for gimmicks, like the use of eye-catching T-shirts at summer fetes or similar public events. The whole purpose was to get noticed: to seize any opportunities for meeting people and letting them know why the CHC existed.

CHCs made themselves known to every local organisation in the book; to every department of the local authority, to all the NHS community workers, to young people, old people and working people, to lifelong residents and immigrants, to tenants' groups or rotary clubs: in short, to everyone who would listen. They invited speakers to make their meetings more interesting; co-opted members of the public to their working groups and put out questionnaires, for example to mother-and-toddler groups, to get genuine feedback on local services or problems. They created a platform for the families and carers of disabled, psychiatric and handicapped patients to draw attention to the often appalling conditions in which they lived and suffered under the nominal care of the health and social services.

This, in the longer term, was to be one of the most important achievements of CHCs nationwide, that they observed a well of under-provision on their own doorstep, opened it up to public scrutiny, and were material in altering the legislation surrounding these categories of patient, and in helping to bring about the improvements in official attitudes and in hospital and community care that followed over the next twenty years.

But for all the activity of CHCs (which certainly goes further than I have instanced above) they were never able to say with absolute certainty that they represented their districts in a personal way, though it was not for want of trying.

Much has been written on this theme in terms of the constant imponderables: "What is a district?" – when it's the size of a city (Sheffield), or a county (Oxfordshire) or several London boroughs; "What is a community?" – and how do you define it? – by geographic boundaries, in ethnic or in common interest terms, and is it a single spatial unit or a series of spatial molecules, linked by wealth or poverty, creed or profession, knowledge or ignorance? "What is interest?" – how do you identify it – how do you recognise the same interest in groups with different cultural backgrounds and customs, whether of diverse origins, or entirely home-grown, but from different social strata, with different family structures and different educational experience? "Who are the patients?" – are they the same as the users of the health service? – are they still patients when they are well, or when they are only names on a doctor's or dentist's list and are seen at infrequent intervals if at all? Are they people with an axe to grind, or are they overawed by the professionals, and the conventions and structures built around them to reinforce their authority? What do they need from us?

In the whole panoply of the health service, CHCs were the only bodies that had to consider these questions, and be held to account for the success with which they answered them. From their very earliest days CHCs reached out hopefully to everyone they saw: could they be faulted if they failed to reach everybody and treat them with absolute equality, especially when they were reluctant to be reached? Could their judgment be challenged if eventually they chose to deal with readily identifiable groups as the bedrock of their public representational work? Yes, they could. It's called 'a democratic deficit'.

I started this chapter with a reference to television advertising. At different times in the early life of CHCs, efforts were made to persuade the DHSS or the RHAs to engage in promotional advertising for CHCs. In the belief that television might be the most effective medium to get the concept across to the public, the North-East Thames group of CHC Secretaries suggested to the RHA that the four Thames regional authorities might consider jointly funding television advertising for CHCs in London and the south-east. ACHCEW, once in operation, was aware that the DHSS had an advertising budget, and that it also had the ability to take time on both BBC and ITV channels without payment on matters of national importance. While it was evident that the existence of CHCs would not fall into the latter category, the suggestion was that as a new public service, they merited some effort to have them brought to general attention through the medium of public service announcements which could also be made on any channel, and the cost of which would be only the cost of set-up and filming.

I have found no evidence to show that the idea was taken up, and to the best of my knowledge, CHC budgets never ran beyond a certain amount of poster and local newspaper advertising, which was as far as they were able to go. The Yorkshire Regional Group of CHCs managed to engage the flamboyant disc jockey, fixer and marathon athlete Jimmy Savile to appear on their posters, and following their example, ACHCEW produced posters featuring the actress Nerys Hughes and football icons of the day Brian Clough and Kevin Keegan. None of these celebrities made any charge for featuring in CHC advertising, and it can be seen from CHC annual reports that many local TV and radio personalities took part in CHC events around the country to show their good will and support, or lent their names to CHC campaigns to arouse public interest, without asking anything in return.

In my time at ACHCEW we managed a fair amount of exposure through news items in the national press, and on national or regional TV. In common with Toby Harris, Donna Covey, and others who held the same position, I made quite a number of TV appearances on BBC and commercial channels, notably in London, the Midlands and the North East. Philip Hunt, the first secretary of Edgware and Hendon CHC in North London (now Lord Hunt of Kings Heath and a former House of Lords health minister) also made frequent appearances in later days, when he became Director of NAHA – the National Association of Health Authorities [and later Trusts]. For a time I was a member of London Weekend's advisory group on public service advertising. But I still have no knowledge of any national TV publicity ever being undertaken for CHCs. One or more regional authorities might have purchased advertising time on local stations for the councils in their regions, but if so, I have never been aware of it.

On the other hand, CHCs were greatly strengthened during their first ten years by the monthly publication of *CHC News*. Published initially by a small team based at the

King's Fund in London, and taken over by ACHCEW when it came into being, *CHC News* was to become a major source of strength and a convincing advertisement for CHCs, as its wide circulation at the DHSS, in professional and academic circles, and among health reporters and analysts in medical journals and the national press demonstrated.

CHC News told the world (and other CHCs) what community health councils were doing in different parts of the country; the problems they faced, and the solutions they chose. It carried general interest articles, a centre-spread feature and a CHC-friendly editorial column each month, as well as readers' letters, and directory information for CHCs. As a confidence builder it was tremendous, letting CHCs know what was happening elsewhere; how issues or problems had been tackled, what successes had been achieved; in some cases offering editorial comment and in others inviting readers' views. Health managers and professionals contributed, frequently confirming or endorsing the CHC approach.

CHC News was fortunate to be edited initially by the immensely gifted Ruth Levitt, who fixed its reputation at a high level. After she left in 1978 to take up an academic post with the School for Advanced Urban Studies at Bristol University, succeeding editors Vivian Sanders, Dave Bradney and Gill Kent maintained the high standards she had set. But the DHSS grant that paid for *CHC News* was withdrawn by the Conservative government in 1982, and after struggling for twelve months on a subscription footing, the magazine ceased publication in March 1984. Ninety-four editions in all were published, and the complete set is nowadays a collector's item.

There will be more to say about *CHC News* in this and succeeding chapters, but its introduction in the context of CHCs' efforts to make themselves known takes us back to the very beginning of the story. From the earliest stage of their gestation, continuous debate raged on how truly independent they were going to be, and how they were going to present themselves to the world. The concept of patient-representative bodies had first surfaced in the 1960s as it began to be apparent that the traditional pattern of hospital management committees (with public representation through the membership) was not working effectively. It began to solidify after a Conservative government took office in the summer of 1970. A brief sketch of this process follows.

The suggestion that community health councils should be created and established as a part of the total NHS picture was aired in a 1971 consultative document, in which the new government set out its commentary on the reorganisation of the NHS proposed by its Labour predecessor, and its own view on the form reorganisation ought to take. After the ensuing consultation, amended proposals were included in the Reorganisation White Paper issued in 1972.

At this stage, the model favoured for CHCs did not differ much from that of the nationalised industry consultative councils, but embodied a slightly greater degree of independence from management, similar to that enjoyed by the Post Office Users Councils. Ministers were determined that the management of the NHS should be completely professional and service-centred, and they rejected any suggestion that health authorities should have any representational function.

This made the creation of separate representative bodies a necessity, but did not seem to rule out their establishment and the appointment of their members by the health authorities themselves. However, taking note of outside criticism, the White Paper model did provide for half the CHC membership to be appointed by local authorities, with that of the other half being undertaken jointly by the health authorities in collaboration with local voluntary organisations.

The Reorganisation Bill as first presented to the House of Lords had had little to say about CHCs other than that they were to be set up in each health district to represent the interests in the health service of the public in the district, and that all their working requirements would be elaborated in regulations. By the end of February 1973 however, the Lords had forced amendments shifting the key responsibilities for the establishment, staffing, finance and accommodation of CHCs to the Secretary of State but giving him the power to delegate these matters to regional health authorities.

Procedures for the appointment of CHC members were also to be defined in the Bill. These amendments decisively shifted control over community health councils away from the locally based area health authorities and it was in this form that they returned to the House of Commons on the last leg of their journey into law.

Much detailed attention was given to their functions and their 'operating instructions' at the Commons committee stage in May and June 1973. As the Bill had made its way through both houses its passage had been marked by members' dissatisfaction at the lack of independence and authority given to CHCs, effectively articulated in the Lords by Baroness Eirene White and in the Commons by Christopher Mayhew, both at the time speaking for Labour (Mr Mayhew was later to change his allegiance to the Liberal party).

At this stage, ministers were anxious to get the deliberative passage of the Bill over, and perhaps regarding CHCs as a relatively unimportant component of the total structure, were less immovable than they might otherwise have been in the face of popular amendments. Rudolf Klein and Janet Lewis quote 'a minister' as saying of CHCs that they had "no fixed ideas about how they should be constituted or how they should work". The government was therefore happier to make concessions on this part of the Bill than on the management arrangements. "And," added the minister, "it always helps politically to be able to make some concessions."

Prof. Klein and Ms Lewis went on to make this interesting point: "while CHCs may have started out as a symbolic nod in the general direction of democracy and participation, their development suggests that symbolic substitutes for action may paradoxically turn into a practical commitment to action." They discreetly quote 'one of those involved', who might well have been the same minister, as saying: "We were forced to take an interest in them because of the interest taken in them" (by other parties).

The minister responsible for the Commons committee stage of the Bill was Michael Alison, the Parliamentary Under Secretary, and it is possible to infer that he is the minister quoted above. Mr Alison is reputed to have been one of the quicker-witted members of the government at the time, and according to one account "a model of urbanity" and "a skilled debater" who on occasion was able to outgun Richard Crossman in parliamentary byplay.

I asked Mr Alison for his recollections of this phase of the Bill's progress. I put it to him that the outcome "seems to owe a lot to you, and it almost seems at times that you were thinking on your feet and elaborating the idea as you went along." I also asked him whether in his view what emerged was a 'back of an envelope' inspiration, or whether it had been strategically thought out. Mr Alison modestly answered that his recollection of the conception and birth of CHCs is now vague, but that he was certain he had not created its parameters "on the hoof in the committee stage proceedings". He would "certainly have spoken to no set-piece briefing" since committee stages are essentially informal and conversational, but "the departmental background papers would have been exhaustive and fully comprehensive, with the genesis of any new concept or departure having deep roots in time and in different sections of the department. The junior minister's role would have included plenty of prior meetings [and] thereafter careful study of the final agreed position papers".*

After thirty years, Michael Alison is quite unassuming about his role as parliamentary midwife for CHCs. I have a suspicion that he may be underestimating his influence at the time, and if so, then the solutions he produced for the committee proved remarkably apt and durable, given that community health councils remained in existence for all but thirty years, virtually unchanged in an otherwise constantly changing health service.

The NHS Reorganisation Bill had its third Commons reading on 19 June 1973, and became law on 5 July. Regulations and guidance on the new management and structural arrangements were issued subsequently, with the CHC regulations S.I.(1973) No.2217 being published, as we have seen, on the final working day of the year. The guidance circular for the establishment and functions of CHCs (HRC(74)4) was issued in January 1974, and the ball at that stage landed in the court of the regional health authorities (RHAs). Not long afterwards, the Prime Minister, Edward Heath, called a general election, which took place on 28 February 1974, returning a Labour government.

---

* Rod Griffiths, a former chairman of the Association of CHCs and himself a doctor, has persistently argued that a significant amount of the credit for the form in which CHCs finally emerged belongs to Sir George Godber, who was Chief Medical Officer at the DHSS at the time, and who in Rod's words "put his job on the line" to get them into the legislation in a satisfactory form. At the time of writing, Sir George is 97 years old and living in Cambridge, and I asked him how far Rod's interpretation was correct. What he told me was this: "I am very short of memories, and while Rod's account seems familiar, I cannot claim credit for events I can't remember. I certainly was supportive of CHCs, but that's all I can honestly say." It is not unreasonable to suppose that Sir George's influence at the time was material to the consistent strengthening of CHCs which took place as the legislation progressed and in its implementation.

This was a significant change, and under the new Secretary of State Barbara Castle and her Minister of State Dr David Owen, some perceptibly new thinking on health authorities, CHCs, and the relationship between them, began filtering through the DHSS. It found its expression in the May 1974 consultation paper "Democracy in the National Health Service" (which incidentally was on sale at the time in the Stationery Office at 11p. per copy).

This contained a number of proposals for debate, but also included the announcement of several decisions already taken with the purpose of strengthening the role of CHCs, namely:

(i)   that councils should appoint their Secretaries by open competition.
(ii) that a spokesman for the district management team should be required to attend meetings of the CHC if invited, and should answer questions in public.
(iii) that RHAs should consult with the relevant CHCs before making appointments to area health authorities.
(iv) that NHS employees and family practitioners should be eligible for membership of CHCs.
(v)   that CHCs should be consulted by health authorities about all hospital closures, but that if a CHC wishes to object, then it will be expected to make a detailed and constructive counter proposal.

Point (v) above was the source of much wrangling between CHCs and health authorities as to whether the former had either adequate information or sufficient resources to comply with this requirement; and among academics, some of whom considered it a trap laid by the government to make it exceedingly difficult for a CHC to object to a closure proposal, while others considered it reasonable. The decision was printed as above, but an addition was later made, to incorporate a material change of use of hospital premises or services into it.

In the consultative section of the paper, the government made it clear that it expected health authorities to consult CHCs at the formative stage of any proposals, when the CHC's views could influence decisions. This also was to become a bone of contention over the years, with CHCs complaining that what was put in front of them in consultation often amounted to a *fait accompli*.

Arising out of the consultation on "Democracy in the National Health Service", a number of decisions were taken by Barbara Castle and David Owen which had the effect of strengthening the position and bargaining power of CHCs. Three of the most significant of these were:

1. the appointment of two ministerial advisers – Lady Mary Marre, (wife of Sir Alan Marre, who at the time was Parliamentary Commissioner for Administration, or Ombudsman); and Councillor Ken Collis (Lord Mayor of Manchester), with a three-fold brief:

- to visit the RHAs in their capacity as establishing bodies for CHCs, to discuss the establishment process and to identify any points of difficulty arising from it, or from early interactions with their CHCs, or from the regulations governing their relationship with CHCs;
- to meet individual CHCs and the regional groups in each region to discuss their progress to date, and their information and communications needs;
- to report back to the Secretary of State on the progress made by CHCs and make recommendations as to how their short-term needs should be met.

2. to engage the London-based King's Fund, the Nuffield Centre for Health Service Studies in Leeds and the University of Manchester Department of Social Administration to provide training courses and seminars for

CHC members and secretaries to equip them for the role assigned to them, and to familiarise them with the NHS and its methods of working;

3. to provide an information service for CHCs, with the aim of disseminating knowledge and good practice among them: this to include the provision of a periodic newsletter to be funded by the DHSS.

All of these key decisions seem to have resulted directly from the advocacy of Lady Marre herself. She recalled how, having been appointed to a CHC, "I compared the situation with my previous experience in Citizens' Advice Bureaux and Councils of Social Service. While these were independent and local, they had a back-up... which promoted good practice, provided information, general support and interchange of ideas. I felt that CHCs were rather out on a limb..."

Lady Marre was a friend of Professor Brian Abel-Smith, who at the time was an adviser to the health ministers, and she wrote to him on the subject. "The upshot was," she continued, "that David Owen" (with the support of Barbara Castle) "decided to appoint some temporary advisers to consider the way forward... one with a local authority background and one from the voluntary sector. I [suggested some names] but they were not well received, and finally... I accepted... the task. This was not what I anticipated when I wrote to Professor Abel-Smith!"

Lady Marre remembers that there was no mention of any particular support (financial or otherwise) for CHCs, either in the legislation or in any of the consequent DHSS circulars. This, it seemed, was not considered necessary, because the role of CHCs was originally seen as purely advisory, their only statutory power being their ability to delay the closure of a hospital. She and Councillor Collis therefore made approaches to the King's Fund for support and to ministers for additional finance. In both cases, they were successful.

The government also set up the machinery for the creation of ACHCEW, subject to the consent of a majority of interested CHCs. Provision was made for Lady Marre and Councillor Collis to assume the positions of Chairman and Vice-Chairman of the steering group that would be needed to advance the project, and the benefits of a national organisation were briefly addressed in the final report by the ministerial advisers (March 1975).

Their report makes interesting reading, and demonstrates clearly the reasonable, responsible and rather frugal attitudes the early members and secretaries of CHCs took in relation to every important aspect of their work. For these reasons, as well as for its historical interest, the report forms Appendix 1 to this book.

By virtue of her experience as a ministerial adviser and as chair of the Steering Committee for the formation of what in 1977 became ACHCEW, Lady Marre was much in demand as a speaker on and to CHCs, and as a contributor of articles to a variety of publications. Never flamboyant or provocative, she always spoke out firmly and convincingly in support of the work done by CHCs, and the legitimacy she was convinced they were winning for themselves by their actions. Writing in the DHSS publication "Health Trends" in August 1975, she touched on the dilemmas facing CHCs; "the first problem is that the health district is often not identifiable as a 'natural' community. Representing the consumer is also a difficult task. A CHC must start from patients' needs. It should try to take a fresh look at the services provided, and see whether they match up to the community's own priorities."

She made the point, which was undoubtedly the case at the time, that so far "little effort has been made to contact the consumer at the 'point of sale' – that is, while receiving treatment". That situation soon changed: within a few years, CHCs in all parts of the country were talking to people in surgeries, hospital departments and clinics, and in recent years the Casualty Watch programme was an important annual information gathering exercise. As early as 1982, ACHCEW did its first survey of Accident and Emergency departments in London, at St Mary's Paddington, Northwick Park, the North Middlesex and Mayday hospitals.

Many years later, reflecting on the early days of CHCs in the context of impending abolition, Lady Marre had this to say:

- on being an observer at AHA meetings "It was not an easy task as it meant reading all except the confidential papers and relating them to the CHC members' visits and suggestions. It became clear that CHC members, perhaps because of their concentration on their particular areas of interest, often had a more detailed knowledge of the different departments than AHA members".
- in relation to NHS staff – "Most CHC members were welcomed warmly by members of staff at all levels concerned to improve services to their patients. They also provided a sympathetic ear for staff who were experiencing the uncertainties and anxieties which accompany reorganisations".
- and in conclusion – "CHCs certainly functioned as independent bodies. On the whole, they were not afraid to put forward ideas or criticise services and did so without being unnecessarily confrontational. Whether in the long run they could have functioned in a culture of litigious customers and increasingly defensive institutions is something we shall (now) never know."

When she moved house in 1994, Mary Marre had to decide what to do with her old papers. One bundle was labelled "Early CHC Papers". She had not referred to them, and

51

no one else had shown any interest in them for nearly twenty years and she reluctantly had them destroyed. Recently she has sent what remains to me, but it is a great pity from a historical point of view that the main body of her papers is now lost to all of us.

As has been seen, Lady Marre confirmed that it was David Owen rather than Barbara Castle who promoted the idea of ministerial advisers within the government, and that he was highly supportive of their activity and recommendations. This is an interesting precedent for the lead on CHC issues being taken by the junior of the two responsible ministers, which also took place under the Conservative government in 1979, as will be seen later. The King's Fund, too, was prompt in its response and exemplary in its willingness to offer technical and practical support to the ministerial advisers and to the newly fledged CHCs. The Fund had already taken on a leading part in the training of members and secretaries, and when Lady Marre and Councillor Collis explained that they were working on a shoestring, it responded generously, offering office accommodation at the King's Fund Centre near Regent's Park, and money to pay the salary of a person to organise an information service and edit a newsletter for CHCs. The ministerial advisers reported in March 1975, and the inaugural edition of *CHC News* came out just two months later. The editorial began with these words:

"This is the first issue of *CHC News* – a temporary newsletter for community health councils. The idea arose from discussions between individual CHCs and the Department's two advisers, Lady Mary Marre and Councillor Ken Collis, and subsequently the King's Fund agreed to sponsor a newsletter until the end of 1975. What happens after that depends…"

It concluded:

> "The editor of *CHC News* is Ruth Levitt. She is a member of the CHC for the north-east district of Kensington Chelsea and Westminster AHA, and has previously worked on patients' attitude surveys in South Hammersmith district. A regular contributor to *CHC News* is Bernadette Fallon, research assistant at the Nuffield Centre for Health Service Studies in Leeds."

This was just about the most auspicious piece of news for CHCs since their inception. Ruth Levitt and *CHC News* were about to make a major impact on the world of CHCs. But the name of Bernadette Fallon was already known to many people. She was co-author, with Jack Hallas, a lecturer at the Nuffield Centre, of a small handbook for CHCs entitled *Mounting the Health Guard*, published towards the end of 1974, when they had begun appointing their secretaries and were just getting seriously into action.

Jack Hallas and Bernadette Fallon made enquiries with CHC secretaries and members attending seminars or courses at the Nuffield Centre, and with CHCs in the Yorkshire Region regarding the steps they had already taken; what they and their councils were planning in the short term, and what were their longer term aspirations. Combining the resulting information with their own experience as academics and DHSS guidance on the "matters to which CHCs might wish to direct their attention" (Circular HRC(74)4), they produced an excellent guidebook for CHCs which was easy to read, informative, and best of all, written with the clear intention of being encouraging and supportive. *Mounting the Health Guard* was the essential *vade mecum* for CHC members and staff while they were finding their way about.

Meanwhile, the King's Fund was continuing its altruism apace. Not only did it provide space and a salary for Ruth

Levitt. It went further, making an administrator available to support the work of Mary Marre's steering committee (Pat Torrie, later succeeded by John Pater, a retired DHSS civil servant), and engaged Chye Choo (the brightest and most enduring jewel in the CHC crown) as secretary and administrative assistant.

None of these arrangements was seen as permanent. If it were decided that there should be a National Council or Association for CHCs, responsibility for staffing would lie with it. On the appointment of a chief officer for the new body, it would take on the salaries of staff and those seconded by the King's Fund would withdraw. The Fund would continue to provide accommodation for twelve months, giving time for the new body to find alternative offices. Meanwhile, its staff would continue to use the facilities of the King's Fund Centre on the same basis as employees of the Fund. This was a most generous offer, and greatly eased the launching of ACHCEW, at the same time permitting me the pleasant experience of working for a year at the King's Fund.

I am more conscious than most of the practical ways in which the King's Fund made clear its interest in CHCs, and the generosity with which it fostered them in their infancy. This on its own was notable, but when the worldwide reputation of the Fund is added to the equation, it becomes impossible to overstate the value of its patronage. The unreserved backing of this prestigious institution was a marvellous gift, and in the realms of wider strategic thinking on health matters, it conferred a respectability and a sense of personal significance to CHCs which was beyond price.

The measure of the events taking place was not lost on CHCs. Members and secretaries were attending courses and conferences, and developing their knowledge and working practices. A proportion were visited by one or other of the ministerial advisers, and all of them had the opportunity of meeting one through the regional groupings. New advice was coming regularly from the DHSS, and the mounted Health Guard was being inspected. By the time the first annual reports came out, the ministerial advisers had published theirs, *CHC News* had issued several editions, and although perhaps uneven and in some cases steeply uphill, a sense of progress could be felt. *CHC News* No. 5, published in January 1976, carried a summary of some 94 first year reports from CHCs around the country, giving a snapshot of the situation which many of them had reached by that stage. The following extract tells its own story:

"To familiarise themselves with the field in which they are expected to work, CHC members engaged in a programme of fact-finding visits to hospitals, clinics, health centres and ambulance stations and formed sub-committees and working parties or project groups to study health care issues of particular concern.

"The other major task for CHCs was to publicise their own existence as widely as possible. Some felt disappointment at the lack of public response, but others felt they had made some impact.

"Apart from tackling health care issues, CHCs were acting as the Patient's Friend and giving advice on where and how to lodge complaints. These tended to fall into three broad categories: "grumbles, comments and suggestions" with no specific resulting action required; "expressions of distress and dissatisfaction" (a plea for help, generally dealt with informally), and "protests, grievances and accusations" requiring action, principally through the health authority or the family practitioner service.

"One CHC had already devised a review procedure for complaints. At the invitation of the district administrator, a small panel of CHC members went quarterly through the complaints received by management during the period, reviewed the correspondence and raised questions concerning the complaints.

"Comments on the relationships with area and regional health authorities ranged from "good", "helpful" and "courteous", through "impartial and detached" to "limited and formal", "tenuous" and "remote". Relations with district management appeared to have evolved more smoothly.

"Contacts with local family practitioner committees were generally limited and formal. Some CHCs were given observer status to meetings and received minutes, while others were refused. Contact with consultative and planning bodies was variable and in some cases only peripheral.

"A number of CHCs matched their working groups to the health care planning teams set up in their district, hoping that members of the groups would be asked to attend planning team meetings to express or research community views and aspirations.

"There was widespread unhappiness about the information provided by the health authorities. It was often difficult to obtain information, or the information provided was insufficient or superficial. CHCs found it hard work ferreting out information, even on the range of services available in the district, and were subjected to obstruction and delays. CHCs felt unable to perform their role satisfactorily without information, and this was one of the most disappointing features of the year.

"The method of consultation appeared to be a further area of frustration. CHCs felt the need to be brought into the process at the earliest possible stage, but their experience was that consultation only took place towards the end of the exercise, when their comments could not usefully be incorporated. Often the time allowed was too short, and it seemed that all that was required of them was a rubber stamp.

"Nonetheless, a number of successful practical projects were undertaken. Patient satisfaction surveys, small-scale opinion surveys on service availability and priorities, and exercises in public participation were typical initiatives reported.

"The overriding conclusion was that CHCs hoped to improve and strengthen the links established with their health authorities and to build up their own expertise so that they could fulfil the constructive and effective role expected of them as the public watchdog in relation to the NHS."

The picture painted in this summary is that of individual local CHCs, set up by law in every district of the country to work at representing the interests of the local population in relation to the NHS. They were performing their duties alongside the most highly regarded UK public service, sometimes in co-operation, but often to a greater or less degree challenging its assumptions and practices. The health service is manned and managed by experienced, qualified and respected professionals and administrators buttressed by a formidable range of powerful personal and corporate vested interests.

CHCs by contrast were obliged to subsist on the barest minimum of staff and financial resources. They employed two or three people, whose salaries equated to the rates paid to clerical and junior administrative workers in the NHS, and their residual annual budget was measured in hundreds rather than millions of pounds. If they were lucky, they had a positive working relationship with the local health authorities, who were the only source of much of the information they needed to do their work. If not, the information might only come grudgingly or too late.

What CHCs had on their side was the ability, drive, enthusiasm and local knowledge of the members and staff, and that proved to be worth a great deal. But there was a sad imbalance between the government's expressed wish for energetic public representation and provision of the means to ensure it. This meant that in practice CHCs had to struggle to make progress, and their reports reflect this difficulty.

Somewhat to everyone's surprise, they attracted staff of exceptional quality, many of them highly intelligent and self-confident young women, drawn by the opportunity to engage in a completely new and challenging form of public representation and to influence the development of health services to the benefit of their own communities. The members too attacked their new function with a will, and a partnership between membership and employees rarely seen in public bodies in this country began to develop in CHCs which had a vision and knew they could only achieve it by working as a team. These admirable features persisted throughout their lifetime.

Some notable progress was also made in advancing the status and numbers of the paid staff, and securing additional working resources. But the gap between what was expected and the means of accomplishing it was never completely filled, despite the efforts of many dedicated people. Notwithstanding the actions of CHCs over the years, they were consistently vulnerable to criticism for this weakness, which in fact was completely outside their control.

Another interesting item reported in the same edition of *CHC News* was a debate on the NHS in the House of Lords, which took place on 3 December 1975. Lord Hayter was quoted as saying:

"The touchstone for community health councils in the future is the extent to which they come to terms with primary care; the extent to which they come to terms with social services; the extent to which they come to terms with the problems of local authorities, and the nature of community health councils themselves... an institution which will never satisfy the demands for instant solutions to our health problems but, on the other hand, provides the means of bringing about change by consent... *an institution worth preserving by, I hope, any government when they come to power.*"

(The words are Lord Hayter's, but the italics are mine, and addressed to Alan Milburn, who twenty-five years later was without doubt looking for an 'instant solution', but in doing so only spotted the negative side of Lord Hayter's proposition).

Replying for the government, Lord Wells-Pestell said "We too would like to express our gratitude to community health councils... we are expecting great things of them, which we feel certain will come." the pragmatic voice of the Labour government of the 1970s. It is instructive to observe the connection between these two items from an early edition of *CHC News*, and how in a curious way they encapsulate the story of CHCs from start to finish.

Ruth Levitt was the mainspring of *CHC News* for the first three years. She recalled the atmosphere of her early days in these terms:

"It was a very inspiring time for those of us who wanted to be influential from the patient's and the consumer's point of view, because it was the first time the public was being given a statutory voice in what went on in the NHS, and that was a fairly radical change. So, from the point of view of individuals who hadn't got policy or professional experience in the health service [but] who wanted to be influential it was a fantastic invitation to become well-informed, and to [make] the statutory services listen (in a way that perhaps they hadn't been used to) to what ordinary people thought.

"The opportunity arose through a bit of broadmindedness on the part of the DHSS, because they realised that it was one thing to set up statutory bodies with lay people on them, but it was another for those lay people to be effective. In order to be effective, they needed to be better informed. [The DHSS] did take the decision – I think highly influenced by the King's Fund – to try and provide some kind of information service. That was the role I was in the very privileged position of taking up. There was no firm prescription about what it involved, and I invented it as I went along. I had a lot of generous support from the King's Fund: generous in the sense of the time and the freedom to explore the different ways of meeting consumers' needs as members and staff of community health councils...

"It was a fantastic opportunity to carve a new route into the edifice of government and the NHS, giving ordinary people a chance to become assertive spokesmen and women for the users of the service. People who became CHC members and staff found that it was possible to be very influential, particularly if you were prepared to work hard, learn hard and be imaginative about how you could [exert an] influence."

Ruth Levitt is an exceptionally percipient person, and while we talked, she made a number of shrewd observations on the current way forward for public participation in health, to which I shall give further thought in succeeding chapters. For the present, it is enough to revert to *CHC News* and quote Ruth's own assessment of the impact it made during her years as editor:

"*CHC News* was a really useful tool, because it was a mechanism for communicating good practice and for learning in a way that was unstuffy and not overpowering. It never set itself up as anything more than a communication medium for CHCs, and I think it worked very well. It was fun. We enjoyed being involved with it, and we knew it had an influence on the health service itself. They used it as well, so that was a good sign. I think some of them were delighted to see us pushing away bit by bit, and impressed by what you could do inside a rather heavy bureaucracy."

CHC News continued to serve its readers magnificently through the process which brought ACHCEW into being and later through the long drawn-out anxiety of the "Patients First" years, and into the calmer waters ahead. It never departed from the practice of accurate reporting and impartial comment Ruth had established, and was universally respected for this, although it inevitably raised occasional hackles on the way. That these hackles were in some instances ministerial is perhaps part of the reason *why CHC News* was the earlier victim of a piece of government small-mindedness of the kind that the English CHCs themselves were later to experience.

The story of the Association of Community Health Councils for England and Wales (ACHCEW) goes right back to the 1973 NHS Reorganisation Act itself. Unlike *CHC News*, whose roots lay in "Democracy in the NHS" and the report of the ministerial advisers, the creation of ACHCEW was provided for in Section 9(6) of the Act. In the establishing circular for CHCs (HRC (74) 4), the Secretary of State conferred the power given to him under S. 9(6) on "the Councils themselves to decide, when they have settled down, whether they want a national association and to propose, in the light of their own experience, what should be its form and functions". It is noteworthy that the term used is "national association" – as distinct from the National Council mooted in "Democracy" – and it turned out to be the preferred choice of the majority of CHCs.

As they travelled the country, Lady Marre and Councillor Collis debated the formation of a national body with CHCs in every region. By the time they made their report, they could say with confidence that:

"Most CHC members would like some central services provided by an organisation under their own control... There is general agreement that information, guidance to publications, and the opportunity to exchange ideas are needed first; then central publicity services; and finally a platform from which CHCs can put forward on a national basis the views of the consumer. They unite in wishing to have *a non-bureaucratic organisation with a minimum of formality, with a small but good professional staff.*" [my italics].

They added that a steering committee was being formed under the chairmanship of Lady Marre, to take this expression of opinion forward and report in due course.

Following ministerial acceptance of the advisers' report, the steering committee was convened, and began its deliberations. Its progress was regularly charted in *CHC News*, the first edition (May 1975) naming its membership, which included Lady Marre, Leslie Rosen (of Leeds Eastern CHC; later chair of the Provisional Standing Committee), Gordon Bessey (of East Cumbria CHC, the first chair of ACHCEW) and three CHC secretary representatives: Joy Gunter (from Dewsbury, Yorkshire), Beryl Urquhart (Southwark, London) and Emrys Roberts (South Gwent, Wales). Secretary to the committee was Pat Torrie of the King's Fund. The second meeting of the Steering Committee took place on 25 June 1975 and was reported in the July edition. The idea of a National Council for CHCs had been dropped, and the committee was proposing consultation on its recommendation that a national association should be established. By November 1975, the consultation had been completed, with 70% of respondents supporting the proposition; 9% against, and 21% voting to defer any decision. The Steering Committee agreed to call a general meeting of CHCs in the autumn of 1976 to take a final decision.

Secretary of State Barbara Castle accepted the committee's recommendations, and announced that the DHSS would finance *CHC News* and the information service for the whole of 1976. It would also cover the cost of the

Steering Committee and the general meeting proposed. In the April 1976 *CHC News*, John Pater, now secretary to the committee, confirmed that the meeting would take place at the Friends House, Euston Road, in London, on 3 November. As a "warm up" for decision day, the front page of the October copy carried two short statements by prominent CHC members, one in favour of, and the other opposing, an association. Under the heading "The Association of Your Choice" *CHC News* reported the meeting in its December issue, recording that 112 CHCs had voted in favour of forming an association, with 91 against, and detailing the plans agreed for the final preparatory stage.

March 1977 saw significant progress being made. The Secretary of State (by this time David Ennals) announced that the DHSS would fund *CHC News* and the information service on a continuing basis, and that the association would be funded for the year 1977–78, converting to a subscription-funded body from 1 April 1978. The first AGM was fixed for 15 June 1977 – to take place once again at the Friends House.

The AGM heard that at that date, there were still sixty-three CHCs in England and Wales which had not taken membership. Of these, eighteen had not so far declared their intentions. Although all of those present at the AGM were members, there was much heated argument over the report of the provisional standing committee, with particular regard to premises, subscription rates and staffing. The draft constitution and standing orders were finally adopted, and subscriptions for 1978–79 set at £150 per member CHC. Gordon Bessey was elected chairman, with (Doctor) Rod Griffiths of Central Birmingham CHC as Vice Chairman and Norman Swift of Bury CHC Treasurer. ACHCEW was ready to set sail. At the beginning of September 1977, I took up my appointment as its first chief officer. My successors were titled Director. During my period of office, the title (as with CHCs) was Secretary.

A workload of organisational decisions and requests from CHCs was awaiting me on arrival, including a number of invitations to visit CHCs and regional groups. My first outside engagement was a meeting with Cuckfield and Crawley CHC at Haywards Heath in West Sussex, to set out for members my vision of the role of ACHCEW and its partnership with member CHCs. The deliberative arm of the association was its Standing Committee, made up of the elected officers, one or two members from each region in England, nominated by their regional groups of CHCs, and four members appointed by CHCs in Wales. A number of regionally delegated CHC secretaries from England and one from Wales attended meetings as observers and advisers.

There was immediate work to be done on behalf of the Standing Committee, and its instructions from the previous meeting (in so far as they had not been dealt with by John Pater and Chye Choo) to be carried out. Allowing for the expected inflow of routine, but vital work, the first objective for ACHCEW and for me was a diplomatic initiative, on the one hand with government, the health service, the professions and the academic and voluntary organisations with whom we wished to establish working relations, and on the other, with CHCs.

The object of this exercise was self-evidently to win friends and influence people in every quarter, and to enhance the standing of CHCs among those with whom we had dealings. Gordon Bessey (who lived in Carlisle) and Rod Griffiths worked tirelessly to extend our circle of acquaintance and contacts, and were frequently in London on this business.

Early contact made was with Sir Patrick Nairne, Permanent Secretary at the DHSS, and the senior civil servants with CHC responsibilities. This, from the first, was cordial, and despite the upheavals that took place in the following years, never ceased in my time to be friendly, candid, and valuable to ACHCEW, and I believe to our members as well.

On the NHS front, it was important to us to make ourselves known to the national bodies representing health authorities and the family practitioner service, and we lost no time in making opportunities for formal meetings with the National Association of Health Authorities and the Society of Family Practitioner Committees. We agreed to write self-introductory articles for their journals, and we replied patiently and reasonably to any critical response. We met and lunched with the hierarchy of the BMA and the General Medical Services Committee; drank tea with officials of the General Medical Council, and talked with leaders of the Royal Colleges. We invited the Secretaries of the Royal Colleges of Nursing and Midwives to the King's Fund for talks, developed links with the Health Visitors' Association and exchanged information with the Professions Supplementary to Medicine. We established a surprisingly strong rapport with the Pharmaceutical Society and were put on the regular invitation list for events taking place in their strange black building on the Lambeth bank of the Thames. We wooed the BDA and the Optical Associations, and lectured postgraduate general dental practice students at Barnet General Hospital in North London.

This bridge-building programme was systematic and successful. It was long term and time consuming, but it was entirely worthwhile, and highly educative to those taking part. By the time "Patients First" crossed the ACHCEW horizon, sufficient positive relationships existed within the organisational and professional structure to ensure the "formidable" support of which the Secretary of State was to speak in 1980.

Gordon Bessey and Rod Griffiths were crucial to its success. Gordon had a *gravitas* which impressed itself on everyone he met and commanded respect. In meetings he was genial, but always serious and to the point. None of the individuals or groups with whom we dealt could have failed to regard CHCs more highly after meeting him. Rod was quite simply indispensable. Brilliant, amusing, and with the ability to embrace a complex argument in one telling observation, he was impressive in quite a different way, and what's more, medically qualified. A doctor in our front line was a factor they could not ignore, and a positive advantage on fairly well every key occasion. The CHC world was truly privileged, and fortunate to have the services of these men at that time.

Making friends with CHCs was no less important a first objective, and in some ways no less of a diplomatic exercise. ACHCEW was new, untried and not entirely popular with its constituency. One year earlier, more than ninety CHCs had voted against its formation, and only one-third of those had changed their view meanwhile. ACHCEW was to be a subscription organisation, and therefore a cost item so far as its members were concerned. It had to offer value for money to retain their confidence, but was limited in its scope by the revenue it could raise, and thus needed to maximise its membership in order to bring in sufficient income to work at the most effective level.

Moreover, CHCs had well-established regional links (among members and secretaries alike), through which they nominated their respective representatives to the ACHCEW Standing Committee, and which had been in operation from the earliest days, creating their own networks and alliances, and co-operating together in the collective interests of their councils. Since CHCs in every part of England had been established by the regional health authority which covered their district, it was natural and virtually inevitable that those in each region should initially come together, either because the RHA wished to meet them collectively, or because they had no other obvious linkages. For three years they had been an effective channel of communication and joint discussion with each RHA. It is not surprising in these circumstances that a substantial number of CHCs considered them sufficient for their purposes as a means of corporate representation.

The officers of ACHCEW and members of the Standing Committee took on the role of ambassadors for the association in their own regions, reporting back from meetings and demonstrating the democratic nature and responsiveness of its proceedings to their regional colleagues. The Secretary/Observers had a different role and a different constituency, reporting back to their own councils as chief officer, and to their fellow secretaries, not as being part of it and having a personal interest in its success, but as independent scrutineers of ACHCEW, free to report favourably or otherwise as their judgment dictated. In the broadest terms, the influence exerted by both groups must have been positive, because membership of the association began to increase steadily, and at the 1979 AGM a total of 203 member councils was listed as present (out of 227 CHCs in England and Wales).

CHC News was a useful barometer of performance, since it reported on the doings of ACHCEW, both in the Standing Committee and in its day to day work, and despite its editorial independence, was more complimentary than critical. The ACHCEW office, which at that time amounted to Chye Choo and myself, worked diligently to deal with enquiries and requests from CHCs, and made a point of showing the same attentiveness to non-members as to members. I was much in demand as a visitor to individual CHCs and to regional groups of members or secretaries, and this put a great deal of pressure on Chye. Fortunately, she was able to take it all in her stride, and kept everything running in excellent order in my absence.

For my part, I was glad of the opportunity of meeting CHC members and secretaries from all parts of the country, putting faces to names, and learning the situations they faced and how they intended coping with them. The process was personally highly instructive, and rewarding in the use that could be made of it. It rapidly became possible for me to see analogies, pitfalls, and other ways in which the knowledge might be applied to the benefit of CHCs, and to offer a better quality of advice than would have been possible without this first-hand experience. I believe that this was to stand ACHCEW in good stead throughout my tenure.

While it would be absurd to pretend that there were no tensions or performance failures within the association during its early period, the general standard was good and the will to succeed was strong. Its acceptance level among CHCs was increasing and the political climate in the last two years of the Labour government was favourable. At the time of the 1979 change of government, it could reasonably be said that ACHCEW was well established.

This chapter would not be complete without specific reference to the 'third force' in community health councils. Paragraph 23 (a) of "Democracy in the NHS" makes clear the opinion of the Secretary of State of the day that:

"Because of the very important part their Secretaries will have in influencing how successful the CHCs will be, the posts should be filled by open competition so as to give the greatest possible scope for attracting suitable candidates."

Later ministers were going to stress the importance of the secretary to the success of the council, and the annual reports of CHCs throughout their thirty years bristle with tributes to the work or ability of the secretary or chief officer. By common accord, one of the key indicators for the performance of the CHC was the effectiveness of the secretary.

The editorial in *CHC News* for July 1981 begins:

"The advert for the vacancy could well read 'The successful candidate will have the patience of a saint, the tact of an ambassador, the versatility of a trapeze artist, nerves of steel, pressure group perseverance, an eagle's eye for detail, a passion for committees and all the time in the world'. This would not be an exhaustive list of the qualities a CHC secretary needs and it does not even touch on the equally impossible list of skills which are required. Cynics might argue that it also omits the warning 'this is a dead-end job'."

The article goes on to enumerate the most important capabilities required of a secretary, adding that "it is difficult to imagine a post of similar scope or responsibilities in the NHS which is so isolated professionally", but acknowledging that the absence of a career path in the health service may enable a CHC secretary to pursue the interests of patients more fearlessly than if the next step up the ladder were at stake.

What the article does not say is that in addition, the job was never spectacularly well paid. When CHCs first took office, the rate of pay was that of an administrative assistant in the NHS. CHC secretaries had to develop a high level of local expertise and a broad knowledge of the health service. They were also expected to deal directly with senior managers in the NHS, including financial officers and doctors. I have made the point elsewhere that CHCs attracted some extremely capable people. Fortunately in the event their ability was matched in most cases by their willingness to perform well above their nominal NHS grading.

Jack Hallas of the Nuffield Centre for Health Service Studies at Leeds University was one of the few early CHC-watchers who looked in any detail at the selection of secretaries. A surprising feature of this process in his view was the response to the advertisements for the posts, which he described as "unexpectedly overwhelming". It was not unusual in the north of England to have between fifty and sixty applicants for a single post. The novelty of the position, coupled with the heady combination of the NHS and community representation, seemed, as he saw it, to stimulate a much wider range of interest than could possibly have been envisaged either by the DHSS or its agents, the RHAs.

The quality of the end product, in the form of the secretaries appointed, also greatly exceeded anticipations. According to Jack Hallas, he and his counterparts at the other training centres were taken aback by the quality and motivation of the secretaries they met. His own considered view was that the enthusiasm and initiative shown by newly-appointed secretaries taken over all, was far higher than expected. This opinion, he added, was shared by staff at the King's Fund and at Manchester University, and was an eye-opener for "educationalists well versed in training managers within the NHS". He judged it significant that in the first two years the number of CHC secretaries country-wide who left to take a different job could effectively be counted on the fingers of one hand.

A particular study of the selection of CHC secretaries in the Northern Region of England (Cumbria, Northumberland, Tyne and Wear, Durham and Cleveland counties at the time) was made by David Phillips as part of a M.Phil dissertation at the University of York. He found that although the Northern RHA dictated the procedure to its councils, it gave them in effect complete freedom in the actual selection.

A total of 121 applicants made 531 applications for the seventeen CHC posts in the region. Those selected were mainly male; nine of the seventeen had come from the NHS, and there was an age range from 24 to 60 (with half of them under 35). All the successful candidates with one exception – a former Methodist minister – had previous administrative experience.

Mr Phillips commented that among some of the younger secretaries there was a potential conflict of interest, in that they were hoping to return to the mainstream NHS after a time with the CHC and wanted "to keep in the good books" of the powers that be. Although it would be interesting, there is no way of knowing whether that situation changed, and once employed, they developed a commitment to their CHC. He too observed that the calibre of secretaries appointed from outside the NHS was in general very high.

The Nuffield Centre asked members of its courses for secretaries about their previous employment, and found that 45% of them had come from different posts in the NHS. Local government and the voluntary sector were the next richest sources with just over 20%, while the armed services weighed in at 5%. Perhaps surprisingly, only one course member came from private industry. Whether this pattern obtained in Manchester and at the King's Fund is a matter of guesswork, but I am inclined to doubt it since to my certain knowledge, among the CHCs in London at that time there was one secretary who had been an Export Manager in private industry, one who had been the agent of a political party, and several who had come from the academic world.

It is undoubtedly the case that CHCs attracted talent and appointed secretaries, many of whom had the capacity (though not necessarily the experience), to hold down posts of substantially higher grading in the NHS. A proportion of these were drawn to the work by the prospect of making an unprecedented contribution to democratising the health service, and by the freedom it offered to work in partnership with the members of the council in the innovatory process of levelling the ground between the users of the health service and its providers. There was a lot of idealism among their number, armed with commitment and determination, and backed by an intelligence and ingenuity which could make surprising things happen – and occasionally did. They worked hard for their modest salaries and in many cases contributed to the cause in other ways, using their academic or other professional training to tackle the problems their councils faced and make them public knowledge.

Secretaries had the strength of being full-time employees; being aware of everything the council was doing, and being the implementers of all its actions. They had daily access to health authority officers at district, area and regional level, and personal contacts in their own region and beyond, on which they could draw for information, advice, ideas and a second opinion when needed.

There was nothing sinister about these links: it was a hallmark of CHCs, illustrated by their secretaries and by *CHC News*, that information was shared and exchanged for the greater benefit of giver and receiver alike. Just as the members of CHCs combined in due course to form their national association providing collective information and support, so CHC secretaries created their own nationwide professional society. And whereas ACHCEW was the embodiment of what CHCs and their staff found necessary, the society of secretaries was their own exclusive preserve, until they themselves decided to open it up to other staff members, and was treated with due respect by the association.

The contribution of their chief officers to the successes of CHCs over the years is undeniably one of the most significant features of their history. Many of them enriched their councils intellectually as well as organisationally, and to this day are looked on by their former members as valued friends. In the 1990s secretaries were re-designated "Chief Officer", a title I have up to now used only as a description. From this point onward, I shall give them the title they finally earned.

* * *

By the 1979 general election, the first phase in the life of community health councils had been completed. Members and staff had built a reasonable measure of knowledge, and in many instances, had won some respect and attention from their area health authorities. The national association was up and running, and to that point, successful. The health guard had been mounted and trained, and in most cases had cut its teeth on the service-change proposals so characteristic among health authorities at the time. More challenging events lay ahead, and the abilities now acquired would soon be put to the test.

Chapter Three

Mainly about RHAs

"It shall be the duty of each Regional Health Authority... to exercise on behalf of the Secretary of State... his functions... with respect to the establishment of Councils"

(The Community Health Councils Regulations, December 1973)

Regional Health Authorities (RHAs) were a distinctive feature of the NHS in England after 1974. Before the 1973 reorganisation, management of the hospital side of the health service lay in the hands of hospital management committees, covering a hospital or a group of hospitals, and operating at a local level. The next stage up was that of the regional hospital board. There were fourteen of these, each based on a university hospital, and between them covering the whole of England. Scotland and Wales, being much smaller in area and population, were each managed by a single board, which reported to the Scottish and Welsh Offices respectively.

In terms of structure, the 1973 reorganisation left the regional network intact, with the boards renamed as RHAs. It will be remembered that the Secretary of State's duties with regard to CHCs were devolved in England to the RHAs. CHCs in Wales and Local Health Councils in Scotland were the responsibility of the Welsh and Scottish Offices. All references in this chapter and elsewhere to the interactions and relationships between CHCs and RHAs therefore apply exclusively to England.

Looking superficially at the relationship between regional health authorities and their respective community health councils during the first two or three years of their existence, it would have seemed that the RHAs acted in a friendlier and less guarded way towards CHCs than the average area health authority, and that the CHCs received a warmer welcome from, and were given greater encouragement by RHAs than by local management.

This would be accounted for partly through the RHAs' position as establishing authorities for CHCs, which meant that in every case, it had been their duty to get the CHC started. They were required initially to advise the CHC on how it should conduct its business and the appointment of its chair and its chief officer (at that time the secretary), who was nominally employed by the RHA. A little while later, they would have organized courses of induction, familiarisation and training for members and secretaries, and these processes would have given their officers some acquaintance with the people who made up the council. It would also have followed from the fact that the RHA was at a greater distance – in organisational terms if not necessarily geographically – from the CHC, and in day-to-day terms, the two had very little contact, and equally little reason for falling out.

This impression, even if a trifle simplistic, would not have been greatly mistaken. The general attitude of RHAs was benevolent if somewhat headmasterly, and CHCs were perhaps prepared to acknowledge that they were pupils at the time. In any case, CHCs conducted their business largely with the local area health authority, and if it was a multi-district area, with the officers of a particular district management team. Yet the relationship between CHCs and regional health authorities lasted for many years, and was an influential element in the organisation and *modus operandi* of councils from the outset, and remained so until the RHAs were wound up in 1996. When its continuation was threatened by the government in 1981, it was the CHCs which insisted that they wanted it to continue.

Since I shall be examining this relationship in closer detail in the course of this chapter, I discussed it with many people with better memories than my own to confirm my recollections and impressions, and am grateful to them for their opinions, guidance and reinforcement.

Regional Health Authorities were given the duty of establishing CHCs in the 1973 CHC regulations: particularly in the regulation quoted at the head of this chapter. It was logical that the Secretary of State should delegate the power given to him in Section 9 of the NHS Reorganisation Act. Equally logically, it fell to the RHAs; the one group of bodies in the NHS management structure whose situation and credentials made them completely suitable for this responsibility.

There was an RHA in every region of England; its purview extended to every health authority and district in the region, and it had no immediate working relationship with the bodies it was being asked to set up. Each RHA was likely to be reasonably consistent with other RHAs in its culture, its procedures and its practices. Moreover, the officers of each RHA had the know-how and the time to do the job, even if, as their instructions indicated, the time was short.

If this gave the RHA officers the opportunity of applying their own agenda to the establishment process, it did not seem to be a major issue in any case, and whatever risk it posed might be considered an acceptable price to pay for the obvious advantages of using this machinery.

RHA attitudes to their charges were nuanced by a range of considerations, which, depending on the professional memory of the managers and members concerned, may have stretched back to the long-stay hospital disasters of the 1960s and the embryonic emergence of a concept of public representation towards the end of the decade. Alternatively, it may have begun with the reorganization White Paper and carried on from there to the model of CHCs envisaged in Section 9 of the 1973 Act. It was certainly embedded in the

1973 CHC regulations and the subsequent health circular (both issued before the change of government), and the departmental instruction to get on with the job. There would have been some flavour of the individual predispositions of the fourteen RHAs themselves, expressed in part in the way they set about establishing their councils, and the completed cocktail was to be modified at the final shake by new guidance from the incoming government in the form of "Democracy in the National Health Service".

The influence of the RHA over the number of CHCs in the region, their membership, funding and other resources was at all times significant, but notably at the start and in 1982, when area health authorities gave place to districts. As an example, the Trent region at that time was distinctly more radical than others in the way in which it restructured its districts, and this permanently reduced the number of CHCs in the East Midlands and South Yorkshire.

In 1974 each RHA was able to set limits on the number of staff its CHCs could employ and the grades at which they were recruited. As the practices from region to region became clearer, the arguments for equality in pay and grading practices became more important, and the point had to be conceded. On the other hand, RHAs' control of CHC budgets and the need for their approval of expenditure undertaken gave them an accountability hold over every CHC as to the range and cost of its activities. In general, this was not exercised heavy-handedly, but the supervision of councils did vary from one region to another depending on the relative liberality of the authority in question from time to time.

Summing up this situation, it is fair to suggest that throughout the twenty-two years of their relationship each regional health authority consistently applied its own standards (which might in practice vary within a small range resulting from changes in management or other circumstances) in dealing with the CHCs in the region, and that the influence thereby exerted was always tangible, even where not to any extent oppressive.

If at the start CHCs regarded the influence of the RHAs as relatively benign when seen alongside the attitudes of local management, this would not be at all peculiar. Patrick Jenkin, as I have mentioned, remarked that health service administrators he met were hostile to CHCs, and not afraid to say so. He didn't say whether any of these were officers of RHAs, but some of them undoubtedly worked in area health authorities or in district management teams.

Most CHC members and chief officers from the first wave will have found the management face of their AHA overbearing or cynical, and reluctant to provide any information which it felt might be used as ammunition against it. I had imagined that this attitude might have mellowed with the passage of time and greater familiarity. Toby Harris, rather to my surprise, assured me that it had never completely vanished. Even in his later days at ACHCEW, he told me, many NHS managers at the operational level were people in a hurry to make a name for themselves, and impatient with CHCs, seeing them more as an obstacle to their own progress than as a legitimate alternative voice.

Their predecessors in 1974 could quite possibly have been forgiven for viewing the newly formed CHCs as an intrusion into the managerial preserve the statements of Sir Keith Joseph and other ministers had encouraged them to regard as their own. The previous government had commissioned a study into the management of the NHS by McKinsey, the US based management consultants, and from then onwards, young, ambitious aspirant managers had been led to believe that a management revolution was in the making. Statements by ministers of both parties as far back as Kenneth Robinson had suggested a switch from the accident-prone fuddyduddyism of the hospital management committees and the county councils to smart, modern-day professionalism as the way forward for the health service, and they were hungry to take their share. Sir Keith's emphasis on management as the key to improvement, and planning as the guarantee of efficiency, in commending the NHS Reorganisation Bill to parliament must have inspired and motivated them, and their ambition was enough to do the rest.

When it became evident that the new NHS structure was to be accompanied by a body with an undefined accountability to the public and no necessary prior knowledge of health service management, many administrators must have viewed the prospect with an uncomfortable mixture of alarm and derision. How could they square a body with no obvious experience or qualification with top-class modern management? Why should they have to spend their time answering questions that would be obvious to anyone with any knowledge of the NHS? How could it be that an untutored group could claim the right to question their professional opinions or decisions? Why were they not allowed to get on and manage the health service? While, as Toby and many others agree, there is and always has been a category of manager who is fired up by a challenge of this kind, managers, in common with any other group, vary in their response to anything extraneous and potentially disconcerting, and in many instances incline to respond defensively.

Furthermore, the creation of CHCs was popularly heralded in adversarial terms. The use of catchy phrases such as "the people's voice in the NHS" or "local watchdogs", while completely understandable as common usage and an expression of expectations, equally implied a readiness to bark or shout. Many of those who took an interest in this new development, whether among the press or in political or community activist circles, expected the new councils to focus their attention on areas of general public dissatisfaction or on individual complaints, and some were disappointed at the extent to which they failed to do so.

But in one important sense the adversarial description was accurate. Community health councils were expected from the outset to make representations to the managers of the NHS in the interests of the public. By the time they in fact got down to work, new instructions had been issued by the government, requiring them to prepare constructive and detailed counter-proposals to management in respect of hospital closures or substantial service variations with which they were unable to agree. Area health authorities could thus anticipate alternative proposals being made to their best-laid schemes, in the worst case requiring a major input of management time to resolve, and extensive delays in putting them into effect.

While it could be argued that this government stipulation would have the effect, on the one hand of making the authorities sharpen up their thinking to produce well designed and convincing plans, and on the other, stretching the CHC beyond its reasonable capabilities and absorbing its limited resources to develop a workable alternative, these were now the rules of the game, and set both parties up against one another in observing them. CHCs needed to establish their pedigree, and as the financial climate of the mid-1970s began to worsen, the scope for potential conflict between them and the health authorities became correspondingly greater.

I have already reported some of the comments made by community health councils in their initial annual reports concerning the problems of establishing a constituency, and their working relations with the health authorities. In the latter connection, there were obvious differences between Areas managed as one single health district (such as substantially rural Oxfordshire or totally urban Newcastle-upon-Tyne), and those with multiple districts. In single district areas, the existence of one CHC and one management could – depending on the character of both bodies – either at one extreme facilitate an untypically smooth working relationship, or at the other, make it next to impossible to achieve any relationship at all. In multi-district areas, there was room for manoeuvre on both sides. While every AHA must have regarded its CHCs with some wariness, it was possible for an astute district to spot the opportunity the newly arrived CHC presented to advance its particular interests. As a case in point, I instance the example of Haringey CHC, where I worked from September 1974 for exactly three years, before moving on to ACHCEW.

There must have been health districts in different parts of the country (and most probably in what were designated as 'losing' districts in resource allocation terms, such as many in London) that actively welcomed the introduction of CHCs. In the district of Haringey, in North London, where I was first appointed as secretary, this was unarguably close to being the case. Haringey was one of two health districts managed by Enfield and Haringey AHA. While it was always the government's intention that health districts should be coterminous with local government units, it was also part of the structural requirement that each health district should be built around a District General Hospital (DGH). The London Borough of Haringey combined the former boroughs of Tottenham, Wood Green and Hornsey (which included Muswell Hill and part of Highgate) and had no DGH within its boundaries. In order to engineer a viable health district it was necessary to annex the former borough of Edmonton, by now part of the London Borough of Enfield, to bring the North Middlesex Hospital into the Haringey health district. In one way Haringey was lucky to retain its identity. The London Borough of Merton had no DGH, and was simply split into two, with the western part going into Sutton health district, and the eastern part to Wandsworth.

Enfield did not suffer noticeably as a result of this surgery. Its health district embraced two other general hospitals: Highlands at Winchmore Hill in Southgate, and

Chase Farm in Enfield itself. They combined under one management to form a two-site DGH.

Tentacles of Haringey ran out into Hackney (Bearsted Memorial [maternity] Hospital) and Southgate (Greentrees [geriatric] Hospital), while some hospitals in the borough were managed by other AHAs, notably Camden and Islington (Hornsey Central) and Kensington, Chelsea and Westminster (Coppetts Wood, and St Lukes [psychiatric] Hospital). Mental Health services were traditionally provided at Claybury Hospital in Woodford (Redbridge and Waltham Forest AHA) or at Friern (Barnet AHA) depending on whether you lived in the eastern (Tottenham) or the western (Wood Green and Hornsey) part of the district. Care and treatment of those who at the time were described as mentally handicapped was provided by hospitals managed either by Essex AHA or Hertfordshire AHA, according to the same traditional split. The RHA covering Enfield and Haringey was North East Thames (North East London and Essex).

Haringey was thus anything but self-sufficient in its hospital services, and from the point of view of the district management team (DMT), it was in every sense the poor relation in the Enfield and Haringey partnership. It lay outside the former London County Council boundary, and therefore did not benefit from community services previously supplied by the LCC. It had no teaching hospital, and no working links with any of the famous London hospitals. Its deprivation indicators linked it with Hackney, Islington and the inner city rather than with Enfield and the outer suburbs, and being neither central nor suburban it was poorly placed to recruit and retain professional staff. Edmonton, apart from giving Haringey its district status, was not a blue chip asset, since it was broadly the most deprived area of Enfield Borough.

The DMT had reached the conclusion that in competition for resources within the Area, it was likely to struggle against the socially better-favoured Enfield district, and calculated that at the very worst, the community health council could do little harm. If handled considerately, it might even turn out to be a positive advocate for some of the Team's aspirations when they were presented for debate in the AHA. So, at an early stage in the life of Haringey CHC, the DMT took a decision to co-operate with the local 'watchdog'. It routinely issued its minutes and non-confidential working papers to the CHC, and invited the Chair (at first Cyril Moss, and later Ruth Bucky), or me, or both of us, to internal consultations. Officers of the DMT were required, following publication of "Democracy in the NHS", to attend CHC meetings, but they did so willingly, and in their presentations, gave CHC members helpful insights into their actions and their thinking.

But these were the days of the Resource Allocation Working Party, and the first stirrings of enforced 'efficiency savings' for health authorities, and tensions between the CHC and the district management were inevitable. Some quite serious differences became apparent when the CHC began to engage the local NHS trade unions in public consultations and open meetings on the inevitable hospital closure and change of use proposals as Haringey's already meagre resources were squeezed further. In spite of these difficulties and the unavoidable loss of innocence on both sides that they entailed, the relationship between the council and the DMT on a personal level remained open, though faintly less cordial than had originally been the case. The DMT did not withdraw any of the privileges it had offered the CHC at the outset, and the council appreciated that although the DMT did not always agree with its actions, it understood why they were taken.

In the limited terms available to both sides at the time, the CHC/DMT relationship in Haringey was productive. The CHC gave support to any positive initiatives from the DMT at AHA level (through its observer), in correspondence and at meetings with the area officers. In annual reports and on public occasions, the CHC always asserted its good working relations with Haringey DMT, but by contrast was frequently critical of the AHA and its railroading attitude.

Ruth Bucky was an original member of Haringey CHC, and remained in close touch with it for many years, between periods on the district health authority and in the wilderness. I asked her whether she was able to recall any occasion when the CHC had come to blows with the regional health authority, or felt pressured by it. The only recollection she could summon was when the Prince of Wales Hospital was to be closed, and the RHA chairman and chief executive attended a meeting in Tottenham Town Hall, facing a stormy reception from the public present. I queried the presence of regional officers at what (on the face of it) was a local health authority issue, and we agreed that it had to be a case where the closure was part of a regionally-inspired reshaping of hospital services in North London. Otherwise, Ruth was certain that relations between the Region and the CHC were fairly well untroubled from beginning to end.

This case study is not simply a digression, since the position of a CHC and the problems it faced coloured its perceptions of the district or area management with which it worked, and the RHA in the background. Because the day-to-day argumentation on issues of the moment and the continuous underlying debate on service provision did not involve the RHA, its impact on the CHC was less persistent, and therefore less immediately noticeable.

RHAs will have applied much of their influence over CHCs before the councils ever met, through the appointments they made and the way they organized the meetings. The 1976 study by Rudolf Klein and Janet Lewis was concerned with the kind of people who joined CHCs and what they hoped to achieve. In the numerous statistical appendices to each chapter there was much information, broken down into the sources of nomination, to build a profile of the 'typical' RHA, local authority or voluntary organization nominee. The favoured selection of the RHAs was statistically most likely to be:

male; aged 45–64; employed in a professional or managerial capacity; grammar or public school educated; with employment experience in the NHS; had previously sat on one or more NHS committees; found the NHS 'adequate' (i.e. in need of improvement); saw the main duty of the CHC to be representing the interests of NHS users to the management and reviewing standards, and most concerned about long-stay hospitals and the elderly. He was disproportionately likely to be elected chairman or vice chairman.

I have made previous reference to the M.Phil dissertation written by David Phillips in 1978. What makes this paper interesting is that Mr Phillips, who to the best of my knowledge was neither a member nor the secretary of a CHC, sat through a series of inaugural CHC meetings in the Northern Region (Northumberland, Cumbria, Tyne and Wear, Durham and Cleveland) and in this way experienced the process of establishment at first hand. He listened to the Chairman and officials of the RHA giving each CHC its initial guidance and made a record of what he had heard with a view to assessing the attitude and objectives of the RHA as expressed in the way it carried out its duty to get the regional CHCs up and running. So far as I know, his account is the only published work covering this process in detail. Since the establishment procedure was potentially so influential in shaping at least the initial behaviour of CHCs, not just in the Northern Region, but in every part of England, this dissertation is worthy of some attention.

Mr Phillips was looking at what appeared to be the underlying attitude of the RHA to the task in hand, and the approach it took, given the time (or lack of time) available to get the work completed. Dealing with the time element first, their instructions required RHAs to complete the establishment of all the CHCs in their region by 30 April 1974. These instructions had only been issued in January 1974, and RHAs had a substantial administrative and consultative hill to climb.

Dealing with the membership alone was problem enough, since they had in each case to determine how many members would make up the council and make their own proportional nominations. In addition, they needed to ensure that the selection machinery for voluntary organisation and local authority members was in place, and that the councils and co-ordinators for the voluntary bodies had done their work. Having satisfied themselves in this regard, they had to reach a conclusion on the issues of (interim) premises, funding, staff and gradings before they could convene a meeting. It was a certainty that the members of each council would require information on these matters, and they were entitled to expect clear answers.

Finally, the RHAs had to prepare written briefs for CHCs giving information and guidance on their initial work programme and the ground rules to be followed, and to arrange for the staff recruitment processes to be set in motion by the time the inaugural meetings took place.

RHAs had their work cut out to comply with the timetable given to them, and there were two broad positions they could take. Either they could insist that the timescale had to be met, and drive the CHCs (and themselves) through it at breakneck speed, or they could take the view that it was more important to complete the establishment of CHCs in a controlled and measured way rather than to let themselves be hidebound by the dates prescribed. If they made the latter choice, they could take a more relaxed attitude, and could complete the process less frenetically, even if at the price of failing to meet the DHSS deadline.

Mr Phillips defined the first approach as 'directive' and 'expeditious', because to keep to the timetable, the RHA had to move quickly, and to move quickly, it had to be in complete control. The second approach would enable the RHA to exercise its control with a lighter touch. It could tolerate discussion and offer choice within the procedure. Mr Phillips described it as 'non-directive'.

There is no doubt that all RHAs in their role as establishing authorities to some degree used both tactics as circumstances dictated, but he believed that in every case the basic approach adopted by the RHA leaned towards one or other of these predispositions.

Looking at the underlying attitude of RHAs to the establishment process, the question immediately raised was their view on CHCs in principle: that is, whether they seemed to be favourable or hostile to the creation of CHCs. It is an interesting sidelight on the entire process that some, if not all of the authorities entrusted by the Secretary of State with the duty of establishing CHCs, may have been hostile even to the notion of user councils, and gives rise to speculation on what internal agenda they pursued in dealing with their CHCs, and what reliance could be placed on them when a CHC was in need of a champion – or even some expert and objective advice.

A high proportion of CHCs, when asked to comment on the manner in which the RHA had carried out its duty from their point of view, replied that their impression was one of honesty, responsibility, and a genuine desire to get the new piece of the jigsaw into position. Members and staff alike described their RHA in terms such as "welcoming", "supportive" and "considerate". Help and guidance from the regional administrators was readily forthcoming and CHC chief officers particularly were given access to RHA internal information sources, where these could be useful to them.

CHCs may have been impressionable at the time, and cynics might argue that this co-operative attitude on the part of the authority was intended to ensure that the newly-formed councils received the gospel according to the RHA. Perhaps the RHA had an interest in making sure that the information and advice it passed on would, in NHS terms, be orthodox and non-controversial. Maybe it was advancing its own agenda on user representation in its own region while CHCs were still inexperienced and uncritical. But there is no long-term evidence to support that view, and in many cases the RHA's approach differed so markedly from that of the AHA officers that it would scarcely have mattered if it were true. Administrators at the local level were sometimes distant, sometimes patronising, sometimes scathing. It is hardly surprising that, even if disingenuous, the attitude of the establishing authorities felt positively warm by comparison.

So, what did Mr Phillips discover as he followed the creation of CHCs around the Northern Region? The RHA adopted a liberal view on the appointment of voluntary organisation members, inviting a wide range of organisations to apply, and placing the selection process in the hands of a council of social service, to ensure that it was independently managed. By contrast, it concentrated heavily on former members of NHS authorities in making its own appointments. It provided a more comprehensive background information pack for CHC members than any other region in the country. The tone of the inaugural meetings, in every case conducted by the RHA chairman, was one of welcome and encouragement, but the content of the chairman's speech was directive, enjoining the CHCs to give proper respect to the opinions of NHS officials, and urging polite and considerate behaviour at all times. No corresponding obligation was placed on the officials or the health authorities in return. The RHA chairman was keen to get ahead with the election of a CHC chair, and this took place in each case at the inaugural meeting.

Mr Phillips categorises this as directive behaviour, and points out that the proportion of RHA nominees elected chair of the council, while everywhere disproportionate to their numbers, was extremely high (ten, from seventeen councils) in the Northern Region. Having taken part in numerous inaugural meetings (including one for a CHC) myself, I am convinced that had the chairman not suggested it, CHC members themselves would have pressed for an election that day, and that there would have been forces within the council already prepared to seek and make nominations. The outcome might conceivably have been the same, but the regional result is striking, since the number of RHA nominees elected is double the national average, while the national average itself is almost double the percentage proportionate to the level of RHA nominees appointed to CHCs.

Having elected its chair, the CHC was impressed with the need to appoint a secretary as soon as possible, and an appointment committee was set up. It is of interest, though not statistically significant, that the majority of secretaries appointed in the Northern Region came from NHS backgrounds.

Mr Phillips's conclusion is that the RHA in establishing its CHCs was in principle non-directive, but wanted to get things done quickly. In its appointments to CHCs it went for people with NHS experience, and in its presentations it tended to nudge them towards a 'NHS management' rather than a 'consumer representative' viewpoint. He believed the RHA welcomed the creation of CHCs, but with the accent on the word "Health" rather than on "Community".

The next absorbing question is what the other RHAs did, and how liberal were they in establishing their CHCs. Mr Phillips threw disappointingly little light on this, apart from one or two comments which may or may not be borne out by the recollections of others. He stated as a matter of fact that the approach RHAs adopted to timescales and consultation differed considerably. As a very general indicator, he said that RHAs which took a relatively long time to establish

CHCs, did so in order to fulfil their consultative commitments. In the same sentence, however, he said that West Midlands RHA (West Midlands, Warwickshire, Worcestershire, Staffordshire, Shropshire and Herefordshire) "deliberately procrastinated" because it did not approve of the concept of CHCs. On the question of membership, he drew attention to the well-documented divergence in council size from region to region, quoting Rudolf Klein and Janet Lewis to the effect that this seems "related less to population than to the policies of the various regions."

Some regions, of which South West Thames (South West London, Surrey and West Sussex) is an example, worked from the recommended minimum, giving their CHCs a membership of 24, while North Western Region (Greater Manchester and Lancashire) among others set theirs at the top end, with 30 members.

Finally, he looked at the selection of members from voluntary organisations. In this area, the Northern Region was the least directive of the RHAs. Mersey Region (Liverpool and Cheshire) pruned its list, reducing it from approaching 120 eligible voluntary bodies to about 20. Yorkshire was "even more restrictive", in the extreme case inviting only eleven groups to make the selection. Across the board, Yorkshire RHA had a heavy bias towards hospital-oriented and 'traditional philanthropic' organisations such as Rotary or WIs. This angered a number of specific illness bodies which found themselves excluded. Yorkshire also upset regional councils of social service by undertaking the entire selection process itself, and excluding some groups which had a significant interest in health matters. The RHA, according to Mr Phillips, was "extremely secretive about its appointment procedure".

Some additional scraps of information about this part of the establishment process are worthy of mention: Rudolf Klein and Janet Lewis remarked that South Western RHA (Counties of Avon, Somerset, Devon and Cornwall) reserved a special category in its voluntary membership for Leagues of Friends, but in fact achieved a lower proportion of members in that category than Wessex RHA (Hampshire, Wiltshire and Dorset), which did not. Like Yorkshire, Oxford RHA (Oxfordshire, Northamptonshire, Buckinghamshire and Berkshire) conducted its own selection process for CHC members in the voluntary organisations category, but I have no evidence to show whether, as in Yorkshire, this was done by the Regional Administrator in person.

Compared with certain other regions, it seems that the Northern Region was very liberal in its approach to setting up its network of CHCs. Mr Phillips made it plain in his dissertation that some regions in his opinion were directive to the point of acting "in a manner detrimental to the independence" of the CHC membership, and he cited the effective ban on certain voluntary bodies, which they could maintain permanently if they wished, as one justification for this serious allegation.

I asked Joy Gunter for a personal view on this, since she worked from the start in the Yorkshire Region, which was one of those Mr Phillips had criticised. She has an unusually broad knowledge of RHAs in different areas, since she acted periodically as a peripatetic assessor in the appointment of CHC chief officers, and this too made her as close to an expert on the subject as one could hope to find.

Joy told me she didn't know about the alleged secretiveness of the RHA over the selection of CHC members, since it predated her appointment at Dewsbury. However, she agreed that Yorkshire RHA inclined to be "autocratic", and felt that it "tolerated" CHCs rather than enjoying their company. The RHA in her experience was directive, in the sense of wanting to keep its finger on what CHCs in the region were doing, but could not be described as overbearing or actively intrusive. She had no sense of CHCs having been set back by the attitudes of the RHA, but accepted that its influence on them might have been stronger than was immediately apparent. She added that later in the life of community health councils, the attitude of Yorkshire RHA became more relaxed, and with it, their relationship.

In a passing comment on her role as an assessor for chief officer appointments, Joy Gunter remarked that she found regional health authorities variable in performance, and that there were those which were consistently poor. Ruth Levitt made the point that the selection of chief officers was very much a question of 'horses for courses' and it could be said that communities were less well served if they didn't get the kind of individual who suited their needs. She remembered quite a bit of controversy about the initial selection process for the staff, and their employment arrangements with the RHAs. She also recalled that some RHAs were as ambivalent as area and district management about whether they really wanted to have a powerful irritant in their midst.

I have scarcely touched on the appointment of staff so far, but on that subject, I take the view that open competition for the chief officer posts was of great benefit to councils and their members; that while the RHAs were all to some degree directive in forming, and later guiding the CHC appointment committees in their choice, they did not have the ability (although there may have been a few exceptions) to override the good sense of the appointing members, and that, as Jack Hallas confirmed two years later, some fine and highly capable chief officers were selected.

On the limited evidence available, David Phillips ventured this final criticism of RHAs, that "the job they were doing was to ensure that parliament's will was executed. But the RHAs were interested parties and it would have been impossible for them not to have influenced CHCs. Many of them set out deliberately to mould CHCs to their conception [rather than parliament's] of how CHCs should function." In other words, the RHAs decided to play God, and to create CHCs in their own image and likeness. The reason was that the DHSS had avoided making any decisions on CHCs and had given the regional authorities too much discretion. They should have been given enough discretion to allow for special local circumstances, but not a licence to redefine the role and functions of CHCs. The legislation was admittedly imprecise, but sufficient ministerial emphasis had been laid on the independence of CHCs to enable the DHSS to place discretionary limitations on the establishing function of the RHAs. This it completely failed to do.

Rod Griffiths and I spent a Saturday afternoon early in 2004 at his Worcestershire farmhouse talking about the West Midlands RHA in the early days (1975–80). It is an obvious topic for discussion, since this particular RHA was infamous for not getting its CHCs launched until 1975. The CHCs themselves soon started to make up for lost time, since by January 1976 Roy Alexander and I were representing Haringey CHC at a meeting organized by East Birmingham CHC on a mental handicap initiative they were pursuing and Haringey supported.

Rod knew the regional authority well as a young member of Central Birmingham CHC and later in the capacity of Director of Public Health for Central Birmingham. In the fullness of time he joined the RHA as its Regional Medical Director, and after the abolition of RHAs had a governmental public health policy responsibility for the entire West Midlands from Warwickshire to the Welsh border. I began by asking Rod the obvious question about the start-up, and he replied: "By the time we (Central Birmingham CHC) first met we were several months behind the rest of the country. I don't suppose there was much difference between the way it managed us and how it managed most [of its functions]. I don't think it had a coherent vision of what it wanted CHCs to do. It seemed to me that the RHA was obsessed with managing the capital programme and hadn't really thought about the purpose of lower level authorities or CHCs. These were the bodies that between them would make the health service tick, and I don't believe there was any kind of vision at the RHA of how it was going to come about."

Sir David Perris was chairman of the RHA at the time, and Rod found him full of insight and skilled in handling a major bureaucracy. He described his dealings with Sir David as "a civilizing process", but he was never aware of any larger vision. Rod's view was that the Region took its role in giving balance to the CHCs seriously and in making nominations it tried to find people who would add experience and weight to the CHC. But he doubted that it had thought ahead as to how CHCs would function and it never organized any development events – conferences, seminars or training sessions – for them. The CHCs were obliged to organise a programme for themselves.

Although Rod Griffiths did not want to sound 'completely disappointed' with the West Midlands RHA, what he found there was an absence of forethought and a sense of confusion, as if it was struggling with an alien concept named "consumer involvement", and couldn't envisage how it might stimulate improvements. Regional officials were not expecting any great contribution from CHCs, and inclined to brand them all with the more lurid stories circulating from other parts of the country. Rod and his colleagues set out to impress on them that the norm for CHCs was a team of "constructive and helpful people, trying to do a worthwhile job in a quiet sort of way" and that this sort of effort without too much clamour was a GOOD THING. It was disappointing to him that 'the most experienced and senior people in the system' had to be taught what should have been obvious to them.

Rod Griffiths dismissed the suggestion that the RHA was covertly seeking to impose its own will on the regional CHCs, on the grounds that it hadn't a clear idea of how it wanted to shape them, and therefore didn't know how to exercise control. He spoke of control, if any, by 'a sort of dead hand'. He added that there was a clear change when

John Roberts joined the RHA around 1979 as Regional General Administrator. John Roberts had a vision of partnership between the authority and its councils which could make the health service more responsive to its users. "But that didn't come until several years into the game." David Phillips had given the impression that West Midlands RHA had moved slowly because of its antipathy to the concept of CHCs. Rod Griffiths was very clear that the problem was rather a lack of vision, coupled with its preoccupation with managing a massive capital programme which in due course was to bring it to the verge of bankruptcy.

The history of the RHA and its predecessor the Regional Hospital Board (RHB) ran broadly along these lines: the end of the Second World War found the region with a fairly extensive range of hospitals, large and small, in Birmingham, and mostly cottage and older hospitals in the surrounding towns and villages. The Birmingham region also had its share of suburban and out-of-town institutions for mental and other long-stay patients. Wartime devastation had to be repaired, and many homes, workplaces and neighbourhood facilities rebuilt. Just as in other parts of the country, new living areas were constructed outside the main city area, including complete new towns at Redditch and Telford. The regional hospital board had the responsibility for running, maintaining and modernising the existing stock of hospitals, and for ensuring that comprehensive hospital provision was made for the new centres of population and incoming communities such as the West Indian immigrants who were encouraged to seek employment in the West Midlands during the 1950s and 1960s.

By this time, there was a mixed bag of hospitals in Birmingham and not much outside, so the RHB put its mind to hospital building. At this stage, NHS capital projects were tightly controlled, in the sense that a powerful case had to be made and scrutinised by civil servants before they were approved. Part of the reason for this was that once they were cleared for implementation, the Revenue Consequences of Capital Schemes (RCCS) system of financing kicked in, and the necessary revenue money was assured. The RHB made a strong case for capital improvements in Birmingham and several large modernisation or new-build projects around the city, including new hospitals at Redditch and Telford, which were approved by the government of the day.

In Rod Griffiths' words "they built a ring of hospitals round Birmingham" and heavily increased the regional level of hospital activity in the process. By 1974, therefore, several new and improved hospitals had opened while the network of hospitals in the city remained fairly well intact. The new regional health authority was invested with the philosophy of its predecessor, that the best way to meet the region's health care needs was by means of a major on-going capital programme. Regional officials had the task of managing this programme, not just in terms of construction and finance, but equally in terms of commissioning; phasing out and replacement of older facilities; equipment, and staffing. When the 1970's complications of Resource Allocation and progressive financial squeeze were forced into the calculations, it is barely surprising that managing the capital programme became a regional preoccupation.

Rod Griffiths takes up the story again: "Until the early 1980s, the new capital was not entirely operational. The system never really overheated to any great degree because there wasn't enough activity to make it happen. Once they'd built Redditch and Telford, and done the work at Stafford and Sandwell, there was quite a bit more around Birmingham, and too many beds in the city. They hadn't, for example, reduced the number of beds at Selly Oak to take account of patients who would now be treated at Redditch, and the idea developed that everything in Birmingham had to be preserved. They hadn't confronted – and didn't until I'd left the CHC and was at the District in the mid 1980s – the consequences of building all these hospitals. Because in effect, they ran out of money. The Region never had a strategy to handle that, and when Sir James Ackers became chairman later, they were finally forced to take control because they had too many beds to manage and insufficient revenue to support what the capital had created. But back in the 1960s and 1970s the Region was largely concerned with trying to get capital on the ground."

As I mentioned earlier, the West Midlands CHCs soon overcame their delayed and uncertain start, and began dealing with their AHAs and the Region, and putting a regional network together. Even in this, they differed from other regional groupings in that they began by meeting in small, sub-regional groups, and needed a catalyst to bring them together as one body. This appears to have been the impending creation of ACHCEW. Rod Griffiths said that it took some time to get any kind of coherence. When the election of regional representatives to the provisional standing committee took place, he recalled, there were six candidates. "I got three votes, four other people got two votes and somebody got one. All the remaining CHCs abstained. So on that overwhelming mandate, I went off to London. What seemed very clear to me was that it was necessary to report back [to them all] and engage them. Otherwise I couldn't possibly claim [their confidence] and I wasn't going to be elected again."

Until then, nobody had got CHCs together and tried to make a regional group work. Rod found that even following this initiative, it took more than a year to assemble a regional meeting at which more than half the CHCs would be represented. But issues began to emerge on which they could combine, and once they began to tackle these as a regional grouping, a cohesion began to develop.

Two particular issues brought the CHCs to the door of the regional health authority, and began to move the pendulum in their direction. The first was the case of St Wulstan's

Hospital, near Malvern, in Worcestershire. *CHC News* in October 1977 carried this report:

"In September 1977, West Midlands Regional Health Authority dropped its plan to close St Wulstan's Hospital, a specialist unit for schizophrenia, which offered a regional service, following a campaign spearheaded by West Midlands CHCs and co-ordinated by their regional association. Barrie Essex, Worcester CHC secretary, stated that until his council contacted other CHCs in the region, the role of St Wulstan's as a centre of excellence and the inadequacy of alternative facilities had not been fully understood. Dr Rod Griffiths, chairman of the regional association said the decision showed the value of CHCs pooling their information to mount a co-ordinated response to regional proposals. "It shows the importance of challenging documents which emanate from the regions, which do not always present information impartially."

None of the CHCs in the region wanted this hospital to close, and they had to find a position that would enable some manoeuvre. They proposed to the RHA that they would agree to closure, provided that the service was transferred elsewhere, and the revenue expenditure remained in mental health. They would not agree, however, until they had seen the plans and the expenditure forecasts to prove the RHA's intentions. "Of course," Rod added, "they had no such plans." So the RHA withdrew the closure proposal for the time being, and some of its later projects, such as the development project at Worcester (now the Royal Infirmary), were made partly to avoid a similar stalemate in the future.

The second issue was that of pregnancy termination. The professor of obstetrics and gynaecology at the time was opposed to abortion, and had appointed a large number of consultants with similar views. The result of this was that termination levels in the West Midlands were far below those of other regions. There was much unhappiness about this among CHCs, but at the same time it was impossible to reach a consensus, since an appreciable number of CHC members shared the professor's belief.

The introduction of pregnancy counselling into the argument proved to be the means of reaching a solution. A majority of CHC support could be obtained for a service which offered both impartial pregnancy counselling and the option of termination. Since in the existing circumstances this was not possible through the NHS, a demand was made to the RHA that it fund a service of this nature through the private sector. The upshot was a new service, paid for quite generously by the RHA, which brought the termination figures for the region back to approximately the national level.

Maybe the West Midlands RHA had reason to be wary of CHCs, but it was unlucky to come up against Rod Griffiths in its early days, and wise to engage him as Director of Public Health when the opportunity arose. It is astonishing to think that Rod was only a CHC member from 1975 to 1982. I think it fair to say that no one was more influential in the CHC world during that period than Rod, and am tempted to suggest that his pre-eminence may well have lasted throughout its lifetime. Many able and longer-serving members and chief officers have left their stamp and have deserved the compliments paid to them, here and elsewhere. But Rod Griffiths was outstanding, and in my estimation, unique.

For a detailed insider assessment of the RHA-CHC nexus, I asked two long-standing CHC chief officers of impeccable credentials in Beryl Furr (of Southend) and Barrie Taylor (of South West Hertfordshire) for their considered opinions. Barrie was one of the first wave of chief officers appointed in 1974, and a founder Secretary-Observer to ACHCEW in

1977. He remained in post until CHCs were abolished, later becoming a member of the Commission for Public Participation in Health. Beryl became secretary of Southend CHC in 1985, and remained with the CHC until its dissolution in 2003.

We began with the period immediately after the establishment of CHCs by the RHAs, and Barrie outlined the welcome they received from the North West Thames (North West London, Hertfordshire and Bedfordshire) RHA: "In the broadest terms they were very supportive. They saw CHC staff as part of the health service, and themselves as our employers. They wanted to encourage the staff as well as members, so they gave us a warm reception. They made it clear to us that they were willing to get us trained and ready. It was a new policy area, and they invested quite a lot of money, for example in King's Fund staff development courses, to make it work as effectively as possible." Ten years or so later, Beryl's experience was "a very receptive RHA (North East Thames). They were enthusiastic about the skills I brought with me, and keen to develop the skills I needed to fit in with the CHCs in the region and perform my duties in relation to the RHA. We have had our differences, arising obviously from local issues, but as a member of staff, I agree: they were very helpful and positive."

In terms of policy, both chief officers experienced occasions when there were open differences of opinion and/or interpretation, and the key to managing these was a recognition on both sides that the functions differed. The RHA was an executive authority and the CHC was a representative of the public interest. Inevitably, these two functions don't always fit into the same groove. Southend CHC had had a major difference with the RHA over cancer services. It was evident that the Region was completely opposed to the view taken by the CHC, but it behaved correctly at all times, providing information and revising its consultation documents as necessary; and treating the CHC with unfailing respect. In doing so, it won the respect of the CHC in turn.

There was also a symbiotic relationship. The RHA used the CHC as a source of information or advice in its dealings with the Department or with ministers on local questions. Equally, it might approach the CHC in its performance management role in relation to district health authorities. This could work both ways, and could improve the quality of the mutual relationship through closer understanding. Beryl was less convinced of this than Barrie, but she did believe that the RHA, as well as the CHC, had learned from their encounter. Neither chief officer believed that their Region had ever in their experience attempted to stamp its authority on their council. Barrie was of the opinion that had the threat existed at any time, his council would have taken the initiative for a meeting in order to head it off, or to clarify the situation. Beryl again stressed that when her council and the RHA were at odds, it was over a policy matter, and that while the authority worked hard to influence the CHC, it did not attempt to apply undue pressure.

I asked Beryl and Barrie about the beginning of the 1990s, when CHC secretaries became chief officers, and what price had to be paid for this change. Barrie explained that it was the beginning of performance management, when the employers decided they needed to monitor the performance of CHC staff. This was the start of a process that later led to performance ratings: the measurement of staff against defined models, as practised in the civil service. This was potentially divisive, and a source of real concern to CHCs.

They attempted to short-circuit this debate by stressing the chief officer's role as servant of the council to the RHAs; then, by initiating a process of self-review, and at a later stage, by taking the lead in developing business plans. Later still, the senior management pay structure was introduced, which was divisive, driving a wedge between chief officers and other staff. Barrie, and some other chief officers didn't move on to the SMP scale, because they believed that the process, which assumed that the chief officer had met the targets set, and affected other staff, was offensive in principle.

Peer-group review emerged from these upheavals. Under this system, the review was conducted by people from another CHC, and members and staff of the Chief Officer's CHC were involved. Chief officers were able to tie their individual performance indicators to the objectives of the CHC, so that the RHA and everyone else concerned knew that the key to performance was the discharge of the chief officer's responsibilities to the CHC. The Thames regions supported the individual peer-group review process, and assisted the Society of CHC Staff in discussions on the terms that should eventually apply to other staff members.

Beryl and Barrie both assured me that in the final years of the RHAs, the relationship was more comfortable. CHCs by then had accepted that they were accountable both internally and to the public, and this accountability became a conscious part of their annual planning. Individual members and employees could recognise the standards and targets applying to them, and the aim was progressively to raise their sights. It increased the confidence of CHCs, which in turn boosted the confidence the RHAs felt in them. CHCs were able to plan their own paths and activities, and be held to account for what they had set out to do. Moreover, as Barrie pointed out, it enabled CHCs to comply more precisely with their establishing regulations.

In practical terms, as Beryl made clear, it was no coincidence that the real uplift in CHC community development activity began with the self-review process. For several years, she had compiled an annual directory of CHCs and Public Involvement. Around 1996, there were relatively few examples, but by 1998 she had begun to collect significant numbers of CHC public involvement projects.

These, she was certain, were inspired by the growing confidence the self-review process conferred.

Life among the NHS Regional Offices was quite different, with the whole process being driven by performance measurement. One of the indicators regional offices themselves had to meet was the performance levels of CHCs. In Barrie's words, this meant that "the relationship was one of negotiation more than it was about the ability to work closely together."

Variation in the official attitude to CHCs was a recurring theme of the response given to me by experienced chief officers from many parts of the country as I explored this curious relationship with them. Graham Girvan, who was chief officer at Bexley when John Austin was his chairman and mine, finished his time as CHC manager for the Northern and Yorkshire region under the NHS Regional Offices regime and also served for several years as Honorary Treasurer of ACHCEW.

Graham detected potentially divisive variations in core RHA attitudes to their CHCs and the revenue allocations they made to them. Similarly, CHCs were at some times seen as allies and at others as needing to be kept at arm's length. Most CHCs at some time will have collaborated with their RHA in relation to statements or plans made at department or at district level. The same CHCs may have been surprised to find themselves on another occasion under examination by the RHA, acting on behalf of the DoH or the district health authority. Graham Girvan was certain that the absence of national standards governing the relationship and a lack of clarity surrounding the powers and responsibilities of RHAs in respect of CHCs created an area of possible confusion and at times conflict between the two parties. He cited the handling of patient complaints as an example: at the extremes, some RHAs actively frowned upon this function, while others funded staff to cover it. In between, CHCs offered the best service that their resources and inclinations permitted. Graham described this situation as customer service by postcode.

Martyn Smith, in his highly readable memoir of twenty-five years as chief officer of West Birmingham CHC, published by the CHC in 2000, makes only one important reference to West Midlands RHA, while discussing the CHC's use of its annual report as a campaigning weapon:

"The reaction (or relative lack of reaction) of successive Birmingham authorities to the CHC's annual reports was in marked contrast to that of Sir James Ackers, then chairman of WMRHA to the CHC's 1987 annual report which was critical of the regional authority and especially of its relationship with the CHC. His reaction was to summon the full CHC to a confrontation, where he attempted to browbeat members for their audacity. In 1994, after regional chickens had come home to roost, David Wishart noted in his chairman's introduction that the CHC's stance had been vindicated by events; but that time there was no reaction."

John Godward, long-standing chief officer at Airedale, in Yorkshire, remembered that "things began to go wrong in the late 1980s when the RHAs started to try and standardise CHC performance, and [later on] the NHS regional offices attempted to 'rule' CHCs and performance manage them. This had a demoralizing effect on CHC members because they were no longer masters in their own household."[*] John

---

[*] This reads like another instance of Yorkshire RHA being seen as one of the more difficult establishing bodies. Chris Dabbs (Chief Officer of Salford CHC) in his book *At the Crossroads* (1999) notes that Yorkshire RHA was the first to attempt setting measures for CHC activities. On the brighter side, Joy Gunter picked up one aspect of its work where the RHA could not be faulted: "RHA nominees [to the CHC] were invariably useful."

went on to say that it was difficult for CHC staff trying to carry out the wishes of their council while at the same time having to respond to regionally-imposed performance criteria, and that this balancing act at times created a conflict of interest. He added that on the plus side, the eventual involvement of the NHS Regional Offices "did have some beneficial effects particularly in the field of human resources, finance and standards of accommodation". In a certain way, John's final point had support from Geoff Ellam, chief officer of Camden CHC in central London, who remarked that when RHAs began to appoint their CHC "leads" from among CHC chief officers, a number of improvements took place, especially in the training of members and staff. From his point of view, however this was too little and too late.[1]

Chris Ham, who was a lecturer at the School for Advanced Urban Studies in Bristol at the time, recalled that as early as 1979, the South Western RHA had carried out a review of the CHCs in the region, in which it stated that "the central function of the CHC is to represent the views of the public to managers and the views and objectives of the managers to the public. Since the main instrument for change is the NHS planning system, it is to this that CHCs should direct most of their attention." This was not just a directive declaration, but a broadside, suggesting some exasperation within the establishing authority concerning the activities of its councils. In effect, the RHA made an attempt to reinterpret the establishing circular and subsequent guidance with the aim of forcing the regional CHCs into one particular pattern of operation in line with its own preferences. This RHA apparently continued to pursue its own particular

---

[1] Comments quoted here and elsewhere in the book were given to me by Geoff during 2003, either in writing or by telephone. Sadly, Geoff has died in the mean time. In my experience he was a good and amiable colleague. From his remarks to me, he still had a lot to offer and died tragically young.

interpretation of the CHC regulations, since some ten years later, the ACHCEW annual report (1988–89) noted that:

> "The year has seen a protracted dispute about the manner of the appointment of the Secretary of a CHC in the South Western Region. The regional health authority decided to impose a new appointment procedure (giving) a dominating and controlling role to the RHA nominees on the selection panel. The CHC in question resisted the new procedure for nearly a year and was supported… by many CHCs around the country. ACHCEW wrote to the minister expressing concern that the RHA was trying to make it appear that CHC secretaries are accountable to the RHA and not to their councils; that this would undermine the independence of CHCs; that a new appointment procedure was being imposed in one region without consultation, and that the RHA was refusing to act in accordance with statutory regulations."

It went on to comment that the response had been unsatisfactory and that further representations would be necessary.

In similar vein, Wessex RHA published a paper in July 1990 entitled "Speaking for Patients". This was the report of a review it had undertaken of the role and functions of CHCs in Wessex. *Speaking for Patients* offered the CHCs improved facilities, increased resources and better job gradings, and laid plans for systematic member and staff training, tied to CHC performance review procedures. Under its provisions however, the CHCs were placed in a highly structured relationship with the RHA, within which the region had the power to exert a major influence on the fundamental role of the councils, and the style in which they carried out their business. In answer to my question as to whether the Wessex

CHCs had resisted these new controls, I was told that they had, in due course, been put into effect.

Margaret Lovell began her CHC life at Mid Essex in 1978, moving in 1982 to the south coast, where she was chief officer to Portsmouth and South East Hampshire CHC until 2003, and I worked with her briefly in a co-opted capacity in the latter 1990s. I have constantly been amazed at the work rate of many CHC chief officers, but I am certain that nowhere was there a harder and more diligent worker than Margaret. She typically gave me one of the most detailed critiques of CHCs that I received from any source, and the content of this book owes more to her than she might on the face of it imagine.

Margaret made the point (obliquely echoed by Barrie Taylor) that with the association of CHCs constituted as a voluntary membership body, it could not also be their regulating authority. The beneficial features of the association were counter-balanced from time to time or in particular locations by the negative or contradictory impact of the Regions, and she felt that a more satisfactory control might have been exercised by a Special Health Authority for CHCs, responsible for ensuring implementation of statutory requirements, allocation of resources, performance monitoring, etc. This would obviously have resulted in common standards being applied nationwide, and would have enabled constant review of issues such as the functions, membership; training; staff career patterns and modernisation of CHCs. It is perhaps surprising that this kind of machinery was not more vigorously advocated during their lifetime.

By the 1990s, Margaret Lovell pointed out, CHC chief officers were drawn from a variety of backgrounds, and did not necessarily feel any kind of community with their colleagues in other councils. Additional resources for CHCs, notably staff, had to be matched against specific need, and these two elements led to competition, rather than collaborative campaigning among CHCs to gain new funding from the RHAs, and later the NHS Regional Offices. Closer monitoring by the establishing authorities meant that areas of work had to be specifically categorized through business plans, work programmes and annual reviews. CHC activities were thus expected to have identified and measurable outcomes. For this reason, the options for empirical assessment of activities and for taking on or abandoning projects were diminished, and councils were rendered less effective as a result.

One of the 'poachers turned gamekeeper' by the post-1990 reorganisation of CHC management was Tom Richardson. Having moved early on from the Greater London Council to Oxfordshire CHC as assistant to John Mullins, Tom became chief officer (a term he considered "completely bogus") in the summer of 1977, holding the post until 1990, when he was appointed adviser on CHCs to the Oxford RHA (later Anglia and Oxford). In Tom's opinion, the Oxford regional CHCs were first created "in typical civil service fashion" with the aim of keeping them as safe as possible. He was quite sure that the original secretaries appointed to the CHCs had been construed by the Region as 'safe'; his own predecessor had been administrator of a prominent Oxford hospital – "a highly intelligent and capable man, but very much part of the health service establishment" – he would do a good job, but wouldn't rock any boats. As John Mullins's assistant, Tom identified the handling of patient complaints as the route to building the CHC a reputation and a following in the district. John did not see that as part of his purview, and in the small Oxford region several other secretaries agreed with his assessment.

Tom made the complaints aspect of the CHC's work his own fiefdom, and sensing his head above the parapet, engaged a group of "very formidable" CHC members in his support. With this backing, he felt able to take the authorities on, and in this way began to make some progress with the RHA. "You had to show your mettle before you got support" was the way he described it. "You had to stand up and be counted at certain stages for them to take any notice of you at all. Most people, myself included, crumbled on the initial assault, but now and again one or two of us would say 'we've got to go and do it'."

The long-term outcome of this was his appointment as regional adviser. I put it to him that the RHA must have gradually come to terms with his method of working, since when they had a choice, they selected him for the post. He answered that in his opinion, the officers of the RHA had started to see that their way forward was to raise the level of public involvement, and that the CHCs were the best means of doing so, adding drily that "it was also a way of getting rid of me in my last few years before retirement." Perhaps there was some truth in that, but Tom in those years developed the reputation of a guru in CHC circles, doing a lot of writing and lecturing, and getting widely quoted by respectable authors.

Although Tom Richardson was never the most docile of colleagues, he was unable to recollect any occasion when he and the RHA had seriously fallen out. He said that as with complaints and the CHC members in the early days, so in dealing with the RHA he tended to recruit other CHCs in support. He was keen on this approach, because when the CHCs spoke with one voice, the RHA were usually quite amenable. One or two CHCs in the region had provoked RHA disfavour, and if they did, they had been forced to back down. Tom remembered that the RHA had received a number of complaints about Oxfordshire CHC from individual hospital consultants, and from a few GPs. But these did not, to his recollection, result in a summons to the RHA offices, or any edict being issued.

I asked Tom about the period post-1990, and whether he thought the RHA had finally given its CHCs sufficient resources to be properly effective. His response was: "they gave us additional support in terms of office space and money, but what they didn't do was give us [their conception] of running the job as it should be or asking us how the work should be done, [particularly in] representing the public in Oxfordshire." It made no difference that Oxfordshire was the largest district in the region; staffing was standard, with no variation. "My deputy was high calibre, but that was as far as it went." Tom could see a fatal flaw in the system. He realised that as the authority put more resources into the CHCs, it increased their capacity to expose its failings, and "if you do this, you are making a rod for your own back." He concluded that the system was wrong in principle.

Tom, in common with Margaret Lovell, believed that "correctly, CHCs should have been funded from the centre, or from somewhere other than the regions". He also thought it wrong that they depended so much on the personality and history of the chief officer. But he realised that the RHAs had a point of view as well. "CHCs had been foisted on the regions by central government. They didn't come about [through] public pressure because the public didn't know enough about how the health service was managed. Both sides had to make the best they could of it, and there was always a conceptual, if not an operational conflict between what was 'best' for the RHAs and what was 'best' for the CHCs." His opinion of the Oxford RHA was "pretty low" because they seemed not to want to get involved, and evaded the responsibility to CHCs placed on them by the legislation. They should have done more for their CHCs and given them more support.

* * *

I was surprised that the literature on CHCs contains so little about regional health authorities; their relationship with CHCs, and the influence they exerted in so many ways. Chris Dabbs' otherwise excellent and minutely researched book, to which I have referred in a footnote above, and to which I intend to revert in more detail in a later chapter, says next to nothing about RHAs, and in many books and pamphlets of the "memoir" type, only the occasional passing reference is to be found. I have devoted a complete chapter to the subject, as I believe it important that a record exists to fill this gap.

To my mind, the initial relationship, and the continuing affinity between CHCs and regional health authorities is one of the more intriguing strands of the history of both bodies. The story, as the selection of memories and reflections above demonstrates, is a warmer and more personal one than might have been expected. CHC members and chief officers acknowledge that they were in some measure manipulated and to a greater degree patronised buy their establishing authority: they know that their capability was limited by the parsimonious financial and operational support made available, and it has dawned on them that the relationship itself was unworkable, that is, if the intention to make representation of the public's interests in the NHS a success was genuine.

Yet nothing very much was done at any time to alter the fundamentals of that relationship, and the only occasion it was officially called in question, CHCs made plain their preference for retaining it. On the RHA side, it seems on the whole to have been a relationship of duty rather than care; on the CHC side a mixture of affection and regret: in short something akin to the relationship between an unwilling parent and a fractious child, animated also by the periodic expression of personal admiration or animosity towards each other by certain individuals on both sides, and the memory of the long running relationship. The judgment of history may well be that the linkage of CHCs to regional health authorities was material (for all the reasons detailed above) in making their abolition inevitable. As an unchanging background element in the turbulent lifetime of community health councils, it undoubtedly was part of the continuum that tracked them from untidy creation to untimely demise.

Chapter Four

The "Patients First" Years

"We did not commit ourselves either in the manifesto
or in my early speeches to take any decision on what
we were going to do about the CHCs. We genuinely
wanted to consult."

(Rt. Hon. Lord Jenkin of Roding, November 2003)

CHC News was one of the principal legs of the information
service for CHCs set up following the report of the
ministerial advisers and managed first by Ruth Levitt and
later by the subsequent editors of the magazine. Among the
items held by the information service were many of the most
important DHSS documents of the period: press notices,
circulars and consultative documents; statutory instruments,
white papers, and the texts of bills and enactments. Papers
published by CHCs and their regional groups, including CHC
Annual Reports, were the basis of the CHC information
corpus: they provided personnel and directory data as well as
news of the actions in which CHCs in every part of England
and Wales – and, in due course ACHCEW – were engaged,
and their progress or outcome.

This was a comprehensive library for a small
organisation, and contained copies of leading health journals,
including for example, the BMJ and the Lancet. Review
copies of publications from a wide variety of sources – the
BMA and the Royal Colleges; the King's Fund and other
academic publishers, as well as others with more general
commercial interests launching health policy related books;
national voluntary organisations and think tanks – poured in

with requests for attention, and were commended to CHC readers, or noted as a new contribution to their particular area of health debate. Current journals held included the *Health and Social Service Journal*, *Social Work Today*, the *Municipal Journal and Local Government Chronicle*, and *CHC News* subscribed to a press cuttings service, which provided daily news on CHCs from the national and local press nationwide. It is no exaggeration to say that the CHC Information Service had "quality status" and was widely respected. The *CHC News* circulation data show that it too was on the subscription lists of the most important governmental, health and academic libraries.

We have seen that there were elements in the Conservative government which took office in 1979 that were keen to abolish community health councils, and that they had support among health service consultants and managers. The first fruit of this new ministerial mood was the consultative paper "Patients First", which was published late in December the same year (in the run-up to Christmas). The Labour-appointed Royal Commission on the National Health Service, chaired by Sir Alec Merrison, had made its report a mere five months earlier in July 1979 (some two months after the change of government), commending the work of CHCs. Its resulting recommendations were that they should be "given more resources to enable them to inform the public fully about local health services", and that the additional facility should "be made available where necessary to allow CHCs to act as the 'patient's friend' in complaints procedures": enlarging both their duties and their capacity to perform.

Scarcely had the last glass of champagne been drained in CHC offices around the country, than the government was announcing that the health service was to be reorganised on a health district basis, and that Area Health Authorities would cease to exist. Since the management of health districts was closer and more immediate to the populations they served, there was a case for examining the future usefulness of CHCs. The question thus posed was: "should they continue to exist?"

And so began a further period of uncertainty for community health councils and their staff. Admittedly the portents quickly began to look favourable. As early as January 1980, the General Medical Services Committee (the GPs' Committee) of the BMA voted in favour of retaining CHCs, and by 15 February, the Secretary of State, Patrick Jenkin, was telling a special meeting of CHCs convened by ACHCEW that the case for keeping them in place was "formidable."

At this time the association had committed a major part of its resources to countering the suggestion that CHCs might somehow become redundant as a result of the management changes envisaged, and ACHCEW Chairman Rod Griffiths and I were travelling the country, meeting regional groups or individual CHCs as need be, and talking to voluntary organisations, local MPs, NHS professionals and RHA officers to advance their case. On one famous occasion we met at Durham (where I had been with local CHCs), on a train from Edinburgh (where Rod had been whipping up support among Scottish Local Health Councils) to Birmingham, and travelled together as far as York (where I left to change trains for London), catching up on the position we had reached, and what should be our next move.

The solidarity and determination shown by CHCs and their supporters at that time was an inspiration and a spur to us to do everything we could to prevent a hostile decision by the government, and knowing we had that backing made our task perceptibly easier. We were, of course, fortunate to be working ahead of the government's decision, and not in the wake of it, as our successors twenty years later were forced to do.

On 23 July 1980 (just before the parliamentary summer recess) the Secretary of State announced that CHCs were to be retained alongside the new structure. The threat of "Patients First" had been averted, and the business of adjustment to the new regime could begin.

However, this in no way meant that peace had broken out. By January 1981 the government had published "CHCs in England", its consultative paper on the role and membership of CHCs. A similar paper, imaginatively entitled "CHCs in Wales" was produced at the same time by the Welsh Office. The message carried by both, as reported by *CHC News*, was that "the rights, powers and duties of community health councils have been warmly endorsed by the government... CHCs are to have fewer members, they can expect no overall increase in resources, and they have been told firmly that ministers see them as local bodies without a voice in the NHS at national level". In addition, the consultative papers made it plain that the two recommendations of the Royal Commission regarding the functions and resourcing of CHCs would not be implemented. On the basis of these presuppositions, they also challenged the need for CHCs to have a national association.

In one sense, a small piece of political justice was done. The Royal Commission had been set up in 1976 by the then Prime Minister, Harold Wilson, partly in order to divert persistent criticism by the Conservative opposition of the government's management of the NHS. This astute short-term move had lifted the political pressure at the time, and by establishing an independent commission to "consider in the interests both of the patients and those who work in the NHS the best use and management of the financial and manpower resources" of the service, Mr Wilson could claim to have taken the issue out of the arena of party politics.

At the same time it was clear to all concerned that he had simply bought time, since it was unlikely that the Royal Commission would report before the next election, and was thus a diversion, from which the government, if re-elected, could benefit, if political circumstances at the time were conducive. In the event, the government had changed, turning the Royal Commission and its report into a minor footnote to the departed administration. The Conservative government could use anything from the report which suited it, and ignore the rest, which it did. Mr Wilson's strategem achieved its short-term purpose, but did very little for the NHS in the process.

The first public reaction to the health departments' consultative papers came in a strongly worded editorial in the March 1981 edition of *CHC News*. The terminology used in the papers was described as "negative officialese" and CHCs in England and Wales were enjoined not to let this restrictive philosophy prevail. In particular, they were reminded that representing the interests of NHS users may sometimes only be possible by pressing for government or national action, and that cutting out their links with RHAs may inhibit their effectiveness at the local level. With respect to the association, *CHC News* commented that "ACHCEW worked hard in support of CHCs when ministers challenged their existence a year or so ago. It is now up to CHCs to show what support they are willing to give to ACHCEW."

In the June edition, *CHC News* published the response to this rallying call under the headline – "We won't be muzzled, CHCs tell Jenkin." The article described how CHCs had responded to the three main points in its March editorial, and the strength of positive feeling expressed. The June edition also carried an editorial criticising the government's position on lead in petrol. The ACHCEW conference at Aberystwyth in September was shaken by the announcement of a ministerial decision to reconsider the funding of *CHC News* and the CHC Information Service.

I have made the point several times that *CHC News* was forthright, and that it said what it believed without fear or favour. At times, it offended some of its readers, as an uncompromising journal is bound to do. But it also earned respect and even gratitude from the vast majority of its subscribers because of the way in which it empowered them (both as a spokesman-champion and as a conveyor of knowledge) and held them together. I have written elsewhere about "the Patients First years", since although in fact the threat of "Patients First" only hung over CHCs for eight months or so, for the entirety of Mrs Thatcher's first term of office (1979–1983), they were under an attack through subsequent "consultations" and reorganisations which seemed never to let up.

I am certain that, finding CHCs themselves too determined and resilient to put down easily, and too popular in some quite unexpected quarters to make their demise politically acceptable, the government decided to go for their weak spot, and shut off the funding for their information service. In this way, ministers were able to terminate a commitment made by their predecessors, silence a persistent critic, and reduce the operational capacity of CHCs by removing their information and communication mechanism at a stroke. By continuing to speak out at a politically dangerous stage in its life, *CHC News* earned itself a posthumous VC in the CHC iconography, but at the same time laid its head firmly on the block.

I should make it clear that ministers' 1982 decision to cease funding *CHC News* was, exactly like Alan Milburn's decision eighteen years later, made unilaterally and with no prior consultation with those affected. In common with the latter decision, it was non-negotiable, and the battle was lost before it was joined.

Of course ACHCEW and the body of CHCs made every effort to save the situation. Letters of support for *CHC News* poured into the DHSS, and the officers of ACHCEW met Kenneth Clarke, by this time the responsible minister, to try and reach some sort of compromise. Mr Clarke was expansive, smoking a cigar and smiling, but in reply to all our arguments for restoring the funding of *CHC News* he simply said, "I accept that there will be problems in putting

CHC News on to a commercial footing, but I fully support our decision to terminate the grant." He confirmed that he had received numerous pleadings on behalf of *CHC News*, but he had no intention of taking any action on them. The only help ministers gave was a short-term grant of £30,000 to cover the changeover from grant to subscription funding. Despite active efforts to cut costs and to raise subscription income through promoting sales in new areas, *CHC News* was unable to continue satisfactorily on the new basis, and published its final edition in March 1984.

There was one striking little cameo connected with the attempt to keep *CHC News* afloat. In the late 1970s *The Times* had taken a decision to start a regular weekly paper on health matters, as a sister publication to the *Times Literary Supplement* and the *Times Educational Supplement*. They called it the *Times Health Supplement* (THS), and it was one of the items to which the CHC Information Service subscribed. *The Times* group was in financial difficulties, and was in due course taken over by *News International*, thus joining the empire of Rupert Murdoch. As part of the financial overhaul carried out by the new owners, the *Times Health Supplement* was sold to Robert Maxwell, who continued to publish it under the name "THS" (*The Health Services*). When he learned that *CHC News* was in difficulty, Mr Maxwell conceived the idea of merging the two publications, and invited ACHCEW to meet him for talks about its future.

This is how Gill Kent, who was editor at the time, and I found ourselves one morning heading for a building named Maxwell House in the city of London, near Liverpool Street Station, to meet Captain Bob and his crew. We were greeted affably by Mr Maxwell himself, given coffee, and then introduced to the senior staff on the THS. They took us round the premises, told us about their routines, publishing schedules etc., then brought us back to Robert Maxwell for discussions.

We had a clear view of what we wanted. We had agreed that if the terms were right, ACHCEW would sell the ownership of *CHC News* to Mr Maxwell, and the magazine would in future be published by him, on his own premises. We were happy to leave marketing, advertising, distribution and a reasonable profit margin to Mr Maxwell, but were insistent on retaining control over news and feature content, and editorial policy. These stipulations were too much for Mr Maxwell, and the talks went no further. We for our part had that day seen at first hand the contemptuous way Mr Maxwell treated his senior staff, and had experienced the scarcely-veiled hostility they showed us during our visit. So, although possibly our best chance of securing a future for *CHC News* had been lost, we were regretful, but not devastated at this result.

The experience of the years 1979–1983 taught CHCs and ACHCEW some powerful lessons about the power and the limitations of governments. The pre-1979 government had come in for a fair share of criticism from CHCs surrounding the resource allocation upheavals. Many attempts were being made by health authorities to close wards or even whole hospitals simply to save on revenue expenditure, and to rationalise provision within districts (which might mean that certain services were completely lost to one locality and concentrated in another, and was a particularly acute problem in the multi-district areas of London) leading to flourishing hospitals being earmarked for closure and newly-built units being left uncommissioned. But by comparison with the economic problems besetting the government domestically and internationally, of which the health service's sufferings were symptomatic, the disapproval of CHCs was so minor an irritant as to pass virtually unobserved. So apart, apparently, from building a reputation in some NHS administrative and professional quarters as revolutionary troublemakers, community health councils did not make too much of an impact on the face of the DHSS at that time.

But to the new government, with its commitment to monetarist economics; determined to cut its coat according to its cloth and reduce public spending and taxation, any consumer of the public purse had to be looked at suspiciously, particularly if it had a hint of unpalatable political flavour about it. CHCs were an oddity. They didn't do anything productive and they weren't saleable, which made them seem like a liability. But they were to do with the public, and the public were consumers, and entitled to choice, and quality services at competitive prices; and in cost terms, they were not extortionate. By a simple rule of thumb, they were rather ambivalent, and probably unnecessary. And they were, at times, awkward. A legitimate target for abolition, therefore, in the view of several government ministers, including at least one in the DHSS.

It didn't take them long to test the water. "Patients First" was laid before parliament some six months after the government took office. Its primary purpose was to cut expenditure on the management of the NHS by eliminating one tier of administration. Opinions had been sought, and practically all the arguments fell badly for the area health authorities. In every multi-district area they were seen as unhelpful, and too remote to respond to local needs. In single-district areas, they were seen to be district health authorities already, and at regional level they were condemned as too localised to have the necessary breadth of vision, and too numerous to form an economical superior tier.

The principal aim therefore was abolition of AHAs and devolution to districts, with some mergers taking place among smaller districts to encourage economies of scale and greater efficiency. But the paper ended with the disingenuous question, which was intended quietly to dispose of CHCs as a by-product of the main consultation, and which gave them so much anxiety over the following months.

The first lesson from this was one that CHCs were perhaps reluctant to absorb: that they were not to the government's complete liking. The power of government is not to be underestimated, and this was a dangerous position. But there was a surprise in store for the government as well. It first emerged at the BMA, with the unexpected decision of the GMSC. Then it began to spread, and within six weeks Secretary of State Patrick Jenkin was mapping out an alternative position in anticipation of an unfavourable answer.

The government was also starting to pick up a second message: that CHCs were quite popular among its own supporters. As ministers and officials toured the country they were facing conservative CHC members who were not pleased to be threatened in this way, and made their position known. At a CHC meeting in the north of England, Rod Griffiths was told by one of the members that her brother was a minister at the Scottish Office, and that she had berated him soundly over the government's attitude. In common with most statutory public bodies, CHCs reflect to some degree the political colour of their locality, and at the time there was no shortage of conservative supporters among CHC members and staff, to whom the CHC also was important, and worth fighting for. The second lesson for the government from "Patients First" was that you cannot just do away with a body that is popular among your own supporters. The abolition of area health authorities went through without incident.

The government's official answer to the "Patients First" consultation was published as a DHSS circular (HC(80)8) entitled "Health Service Development: Structure and Management". It left no doubt about their position on CHCs, commenting that "later on, when it is possible to form a considered judgment of the need for separate consumer representative bodies to exist alongside the new, more locally based health authorities, the position will be looked at again."

The wolf may not have been able to take the sheep on this occasion, but had served notice that it was not giving up.

The power of government (as this illustrates) is not so easily shaken, especially by so minor an obstacle as a community health council. The "Patients First" consultation had been a setback, but there are more ways of skinning a cat. If CHCs were not to be abolished, at least they could be trimmed down to size, or to use Leslie Rosen's term "neutered". "Essentially local bodies" was the description coined by Mr Jenkin, and the DHSS ministers next set about expanding this definition to make it clear that in their view CHCs should not raise their sights beyond the boundaries of their district or the functions of the district health authority. The January 1981 consultation paper "CHCs in England" tightened the screw one further turn, declaring that CHCs "will be retained for the time being"; the Welsh one was somewhat more liberal. The government proposed that henceforward they should have fewer members; no say on national issues, and no additional resources.

Ignoring the wisdom accepted since the time of the 1972 White Paper, it now suggested that CHCs should cease to be independent of the authorities they were supposed to scrutinise, and become the creatures of the new district health authorities. These would take over the former regional health authority role in relation to CHCs, including the appointment of their own nominees. RHAs in turn would no longer be required, on matters concerning particular districts, to consult the responsible CHCs. The recommendations of the Royal Commission relating to CHCs were formally rejected, and councils were asked to consider whether, under these new arrangements they had any need for a national association.

Consultation on these proposals was to run until 30 April, and a response from the government would be made later in the year. CHCs were advised that following the Secretary of State's announcement, existing councils would be wound down, and "new" CHCs, matching the areas of the district health authorities, would take up office on 1 April 1982.

Unsurprisingly, this package aroused a fierce response from community health councils. Battle hardened by now, they were angered by the speed with which the second attack had been launched and reacted smartly. All the organisational proposals, including notably those severing the links with RHAs, were rejected. Respondents asserted the need and justification for CHCs to speak out when required on matters of 'national' importance, and reminded the government of their record as 'patient's friend' and its value to the public. Finally, they made it clear to ministers that they had the prescriptive right to determine the need or otherwise for an association, and gave ACHCEW a resounding vote of confidence. At this time, 95% of CHCs were members.

This consultation completed, the summer of 1981 passed without any reaction from the government, provoking some restiveness among CHCs, which were anxious to get this hurdle behind them. At the ACHCEW annual meeting at Aberystwyth in September, there was much speculation concerning what changes were to be made, and what would be the situation in April 1982, when the reorganisation was due to take place. A letter from Sir George Young, received on the first day, confirmed that ACHCEW was to continue, but fresh rumours began to circulate with regard to the CHC information service.

On the second day, Rod Griffiths announced from the chair that the DHSS representatives present had informed him that "ministers are reconsidering the funding arrangements for *CHC News*" including the possibility of changing it to a subscription item. The meeting responded with a spirited resolution in support of the magazine and upholding the principle of central funding. The message given to the DHSS officials present to take back to departmental ministers was unequivocally clear.

124

Towards the end of 1981 a new management moved into the Department, and Norman Fowler became Secretary of State. Obviously he needed an orientation period, but time was passing; 'shadow' district health authorities were reaching an advanced stage in their preparations for taking over local NHS management, and the period of metamorphosis for the 'new' CHCs was getting shorter. The unease among CHCs was evident, and the December issue of *CHC News* carried a supportive editorial, urging Mr Fowler to break his silence.

At long last, on 23 December 1981 (when else?), the Secretary of State made his announcement to the House of Commons. A new health circular (HC(81)15) had been issued, which would in future be the official establishing circular for CHCs. Among its provisions, the role of regional authorities as establishing bodies was confirmed, but the membership of CHCs was trimmed to between 18 and 24 per council. In the course of his statement, Mr Fowler declared that CHCs were to be retained for 'a period', adding that "the longer-term case for their retention will be reconsidered in the light of the experience of the operation of the more locally based district health authorities."

Meanwhile, the first talks between officers of ACHCEW and the DHSS since the January consultation had taken place on 10 December. It was immediately made plain that *CHC News* would no longer be funded by central grant. This was a ministerial decision, and was irreversible. The association was told that ministers had no strong views on whether the magazine should continue into the 1982–83 financial year, but that since most CHCs seemed to like it, they could pay for it by subscription out of their existing budgets. The *CHC News* editorial column of January 1982 examined this hypothesis and concluded that it could only lead to closure. It ended with the following riposte:

"the Department knows very well that there is little extra income to be had by taking adverts and trying to attract more non-CHC subscribers. The proposed switch to funding by subscription (will) assassinate *CHC News* just at the time when CHCs need to talk to each other more than ever before."

The frustration and hurt is evident, just as there is a hint of spiteful glee to the manner in which the ministers' decision was presented to ACHCEW, suggesting there is something more behind it than a straightforward political decision. Conspiracy theorists may refer at this point to my Appendix Two, and the side comment on Dr Vaughan by Patrick Jenkin during his conversation with me. My theory is this: that Gerry Vaughan, possibly influenced by his far-right associates in the medical profession, was totally committed to uprooting CHCs. He expected this to be a pushover. "Patients First" was the machinery he used in England and Wales, while a parallel attack was launched on Local Health Councils in Scotland. "Patients First" had backfired, as Patrick Jenkin soon realised, and the Scottish campaign was dropped, but he was not going to let go.

So, ignoring the pro-CHC element in his party, he immediately came back with "CHCs in England", the aim of which was to water CHCs down to the point of ineffectiveness. First, he attempted to make them less independent than even the 1973 government was prepared to tolerate. That proved generally unacceptable, not simply among CHCs and their supporters, but also among his colleagues. At the same time, looking back to the controversy of the mid-1970s, he tried to use the CHCs to torpedo their own association. This also backfired. But he was not beaten. *CHC News* had been publishing some salty comment on the actions and attitudes of the government, and this stung. Hence the brainwave: a little surgery – cut off the CHCs' organ of communication and their information source – and you have the Final Solution.

How did he get away with it? He led for the government on "Patients First" and forever afterwards could claim to be the chief expert on this small subject. How did he come to lead on "Patients First"? This was the first major NHS initiative taken by the Thatcher government, and Patrick Jenkin was Secretary of State. The answer comes from Lord Jenkin: "he was not an easy colleague. There were times when he and I were literally throwing the papers at each other. He was extremely obstinate... (and) totally against keeping CHCs." Dr Vaughan was driven, blinkered, and argumentative, and in this sense was tougher than the more courtly and cerebral Lord Jenkin, and argued himself into the position over his senior colleague. Dr Vaughan became a DHSS minister when the Conservative government took office in 1979, and served until 4 March 1982, when he was replaced by Kenneth Clarke. *CHC News* apart, the CHC horizon began to look brighter after that.

Just as improvements in the weather take time to materialise, so those in the political climate are seldom immediate. The worst of the storm may have been over by 1982, but there were still squalls to be weathered. In the early part of the year, I began to detect a pattern of enquiries from CHCs relating to working relations with their RHAs which led me to publish some general guidance on the subject. In one case, a CHC had been taken to task by its regional health authority for an action which was described as 'political'; in several others, CHCs had been accused of exceeding their powers.

The guidance I gave drew on the CHC Regulations (S.I. 1973 No. 2217); the National Health Service Act 1977, and the CHC Circular HC(81)15. What it amounted to was that CHCs at that time had the power to do anything or nothing provided in the 1977 Act. The only limitation on them was that their budgets had to be approved by the RHA, and that the expenditure they undertook had to be acceptable to it. Enquiries ACHCEW had made in 1980 had shown that at the margin of CHC activity, the interpretation by RHAs of what was acceptable might vary from region to region, and that the authorities tended to judge "each case on its merits in the circumstances prevailing."

I advised that recent ministerial insistence that CHCs were essentially local bodies, which should not involve themselves in national policy issues, coupled with Mr Jenkin's opinion that they should not become pressure groups for patients, may have shifted the threshold of what was not acceptable to the RHAs. In view of the recent differences between CHCs and ministers, I deduced that the DHSS may have asked RHA chairmen to 'keep an eye' on the activities of CHCs in their regions, and that this was what had caused the sudden rash of problems. As I have shown elsewhere, over the many years they were associated, relationships between CHCs and their establishing RHAs were generally good, and this seems to have been a short-lived exception to the rule.

Brent CHC in North London was one of those whose actions were challenged by the RHA and will serve admirably to illustrate the life of an individual council during this turbulent period. Brent was a somewhat special CHC. From the earliest days, some CHCs had the reputation of being more radical in their attitudes than the general run. Usually they were to be found in major cities: in the conurbations of London, Birmingham, Liverpool and Manchester; South and West Yorkshire and Tyneside. Typically, they were situated in the inner or inner suburban areas, especially those lacking high quality services, or with high levels of social deprivation and financial hardship. CHCs that developed this style tended to have a young, able, community-action minded, or anti-establishment leadership. They did not readily endear themselves to ministers of any government. Brent was one such council. In 1977, with the assistance of Brent Borough Council, the CHC took the hitherto unprecedented step of taking Brent and Harrow area health authority to court over closures without proper consultation at Willesden General Hospital and at St Monica's Geriatric Hospital, both in their district.

Zena Mason became chair of Brent CHC at about this time, and agrees that it was quite radical in its approach. But she insists that the council did not simply oppose the health authority; it made an effort to put forward positive alternatives. As an important example of this, she quotes "A Community Hospital for Willesden", the CHC's counter proposal, offering a way forward for Willesden Hospital which fitted the Community Hospital model issued by the DHSS in 1974, and would have served this deprived area better than the closure proposed by the AHA. Once the hospital was closed, people had to travel from Willesden Green to Acton Lane, near Park Royal, to attend at Central Middlesex Hospital, which, in Zena's opinion, had a major adverse impact on the community.

According to Zena, some officers of the AHA were encouraging and co-operative, and she recalled one of them saying that the CHC ought to be given money to develop its own proposals. He felt that CHCs had a part to play in the development of local health services, and on reflection, she believes that he was sincere: "they hoped for our co-operation, and were willing to work with us." She conceded that in 1976 and 1977 there were many changes taking place, focussing largely on what was called 'rationalisation', but to the CHC meant cuts, and they were at odds with the AHA on a number of fronts. "Really, they were very frustrating times," she commented, "because CHCs didn't have the clout to change anything, and you were just a thorn in the side of the AHA. But we were fortunate that we had two excellent secretaries in Peter Hay, followed by Jeannette Mitchell, both very well respected by the health authority because of their competence and their ability to do the detailed research necessary. They were the key people, really."

I asked Zena how the CHC had set about impressing its presence on the community. She said that they made good use of the local press – "the local newspapers in particular reported everything the CHC said and did. The use of the press was very important, and the fact that we had the ear of the press. We could report what we actually saw." She did admit that the press could be a two-edged weapon: "as time went by and we got a lot of publicity – the political activists began to realise that it wasn't a bad idea to get involved." A few people from ultra-left groups managed to get on the CHC, and tried to use it to fight other issues, such as trains carrying nuclear fuels on lines passing through Brent. They presented it as a health issue, because if there had been an accident, it would have been pretty disastrous. They eventually all left, but at that time there was a very left-wing group in power on Brent Council, and it was from there they got their nominations.

At the time of the legal action, North West Thames RHA appeared sympathetic to the CHC's case. It wrote to the area health authority asking it to produce a consultation document in line with the NHS closure procedure, but later declined to intervene when the AHA refused a request from Brent Council to stop the building works in progress, reopen the hospitals, and begin public consultation on their future. I asked Zena whether the RHA had put any kind of pressure on the CHC. She had no recollection of any such action. She added that the CHC had little to do with the region, and that when they did, the RHA treated them well and wasn't "particularly dictatorial". She was not disappointed with the way the RHA handled the consultation dispute. It had asked the AHA to consult, and eventually, under the threat of legal action, the AHA complied.

Zena's conclusions on Brent CHC might be summed up as 'rueful pride'. Pride, because they wrote well researched and influential reports, notably on the Review of the Mental Health Act: "one or two of our recommendations did actually get into the 1983 Act." Rueful, because: "we were finding our feet. We weren't into all the intricacies. We were a bit naïve on how to organise campaigns. These skills developed later."

I have chosen Brent as a case study for this chapter because many people's impression of it at the time was a strident and argumentative CHC which went its own way, persistently making waves. Ministers hostile to CHCs would certainly have regarded it unfavourably, and may well have singled Brent out as a trouble maker in the light of the legal challenge to the AHA. The CHC was one of those brought to my attention in 1982, in the wake of an accusation from North West Thames RHA that it had taken a political action in allowing a local group to use its offices for a "Troops Out" meeting on Northern Ireland. When warned that the premises may not be used for any purposes other than those clearly connected with health care, the CHC had agreed, but had insisted that it would define what constituted a health care issue. The RHA refused to accept this response. A separate matter, not referred to me at the time, was a leaflet on prescription charges produced by the CHC, which included a page attacking government spending policies on health and defence. The 'not particularly dictatorial' RHA quite rightly felt obliged to put its foot down on this occasion. The issue was finally resolved by agreement between the two parties.

Brent CHC had always been newsworthy. In 1979, it was one of eleven CHCs which joined the co-ordinating group on the contraceptive drug Depo Provera, having observed it being given, mainly to black and Asian women, at the Central Middlesex Hospital, and in clinics in the district. Knowing that this drug was not licensed in the UK for long-term use, the CHC began making enquiries about its prescription and usage. These finally resulted in a reduction in the number of women on Depo Provera in Brent health district.

In this instance, the CHC had identified a genuine health issue, of greater importance since it was a real cause for concern and affected minority groups, and had dealt with it in the interests of the women concerned, with a satisfactory result. Later, in 1983, Brent CHC was one of the councils which publicly opposed the government's NHS manpower cuts. The CHC jointly sponsored a major rally in October 1983 with Brent Council and local trade unions in support of Brent Health Authority, which had refused to implement staffing cuts demanded by the government.

On the evidence assembled, perhaps there is a case for marking Brent CHC down as 'an agent of subversion, continuing to fight the class war etc. etc.' of the kind reported to Patrick Jenkin in 1975. Without any doubt, it was different from the body of CHCs, and quite possibly an embarrassment to some of the more stolid or conventional councils. Yet talking to Zena Mason, a gentle, earnest and committed woman in the best UK tradition of responsible service to the community, it is difficult to imagine the CHC under her leadership as a snake pit of neo-trotskyite revolutionaries, as it might have seemed to the eyes of Dr Vaughan.

It is true that the 1970s was a decade of far-left entryism: into the Labour Party and the trade unions; and into voluntary (especially campaigning) organisations, and student bodies. From Zena's account, there undoubtedly was a phase of entryism into the CHC which may have influenced its posture on a number of local issues. But it was a short-term entryism; "they eventually all left"; and the CHC then presumably returned to normal.

Gordon Bessey, the founder chairman of ACHCEW, used to say he could tolerate quite a broad spectrum of political colour, even in a very small organisation such as the association. Professional politicians appear to be more sensitive, and suspicious of anyone who does not fit the pattern that appeals to them. I share Gordon Bessey's political tolerance and find pleasure in variety, even to the point of eccentricity. Brent was an *interesting* CHC.

One positive side effect of the events described in this chapter was an approach made to me by John Finch, a lecturer in Law at Leicester University who was well-disposed towards CHCS and concerned by what appeared to a one-sided struggle between them and the machinery of government. In an effort to improve the odds, he offered to provide a legal advice service, available through ACHCEW and dealing with issues of general interest to CHCs as well as requests for specific advice from the association or individual member councils. While it lasted, this was a welcome addition to the ACHCEW armoury.

There are three further historical notes to the early ACHCEW era that I ought to include before passing on to the next phase. The first two of these, in an otherwise fairly bleak account, are events to celebrate. In September 1979, Jean Robinson of Oxfordshire CHC and Trevor Gray of South Gwent CHC in Wales were appointed as lay members of the General Medical Council (GMC) by the Privy Council. The GMC having been enlarged following the government's acceptance of the Merrison report, nominations had been requested from ACHCEW through the DHSS for two of the new laypersons' seats. ACHCEW was delighted at the time to have been invited to make nominations for these appointments, and gratified subsequently to learn that both had been successful. Three years later, as a very definite sign of the increasing warmth of the relationship between CHCs and GPs, ACHCEW was invited by the Royal College of General Practitioners to collaborate in the creation of a Patient Liaison Group within the RCGP. Anne Crerar, chair of Central Birmingham CHC, and Sue Jenkins, chief officer of Leeds Western CHC had been engaged in preparing for the formation of the Group, whose purpose was to increase collaboration between patients and doctors nationally and locally. Membership was to comprise equal numbers of doctors and lay representatives, with the latter being nominated by ACHCEW. John Austin, who was chair of ACHCEW at the time, was a member of the team that launched the new group at a press conference held at the Royal College in December 1982.

In February 1983, the Secretary of State Norman Fowler set up an inquiry into the management of the NHS under the chairmanship of Roy (later Sir Roy) Griffiths, then managing director of the supermarket group, Sainsbury's. The inquiry team was given a brief "to examine how NHS resources are used and controlled, and to identify how management practice can ensure the best value for money and the best possible services for patients". The team looked into management from the DHSS to the hospital unit, as well as GP and community services, making a series of studies in each sector and in different parts of the country, the results of which formed part of its report. There was much anxiety among CHCs that the inquiry might lead to loss of their consultation rights, since one of the Griffiths objectives was to speed up decision making, and the obligation to consult had always been a source of contention between CHCs and health authorities in a hurry. In the event, the rules were streamlined, but the obligation remained.

Reviewing this period of the history of CHCs, I have realised the extent to which we were kept on the defensive by the battery of recurrent government initiatives that seemed constantly to be posing a new threat or making new demands on our minimal resources. An interesting climatic indicator can be seen in the titles of some of the most important papers I wrote between 1979 and 1983, and for interest, I have selected five of them, listed in chronological order with dates and purposes as follows:

"What next for CHCs?" – address to the Royal Society of Health Conference, May 1979.

"Patients First and Foremost" – paper for the Special Meeting of ACHCEW, February 1980.

"In defence of the CHC" – letter to the *British Medical Journal*, February 1980.

"Clamp-down hits CHCs" – article for *CHC News*, March 1982.

"Fighting to be accepted" – article for the *Health and Social Service Journal*, June 1982.

It would be difficult to say with any certainty which, if any, of them had the greatest impact. "What next?" attracted most attention, including a waspish editorial in the BMJ in June that year. At this distance it seems odd, since none of the suggestions that upset the BMJ at the time were unreasonable, and they have all become reality in later years.

Kenneth Clarke came to address the ACHCEW annual meeting in Sheffield in 1983. It was my final appearance as secretary of the association. We had tea together before he spoke, and he was at ease and relaxed as ever. He told the meeting to put its collective mind at rest, because "the future of CHCs is not at any risk whatsoever". No direct new threats had been made since he had joined the ministerial team eighteen months or so earlier, and the assembled CHCs took his word when he told them "we value your role as consumer watchdog" and "we wish for close and continuing contacts". The relief was almost audible, and saved him any embarrassment he might have expected over his endorsement of his predecessor's decision to stop funding *CHC News*. At Sheffield, Mr Clarke was a popular minister, enjoying the appreciation of his audience. The government and the CHCs were finally at peace for a while. The "Patients First" years were over.

* * *

I have covered the history of community health councils from 1971 to 1983 in relatively greater detail than subsequently for two reasons: first, because I was there at the time and much of what I have written is personal to me, and second, because this was the period of gestation, birth and childhood, and as with any organism, this is the time when all the most influential events (birth, nurturing, education and forming for later life) take place. I am convinced that an understanding of this period is essential to a full appreciation of what CHCs became in their mature years, and the way they came to their end.

I am equally certain that the events and personalities of recent years will be more familiar to many readers than those touched on in the preceding pages, and will not require the same measure of elaboration. My intention is that the contents of the first four chapters of this book will go some way towards making the entire work more readable and satisfying, and will give it a sound final balance.

Chapter Five

Into the Doldrums

"They are in a metaphorical sense a relic of the last great campaign for community participation... they have been left to their own devices and ignored by the outside world."

(Fedelma Winkler, 1989)

The carnage resulting from the April 1982 NHS management shift from Area to District health authorities was not nearly so extensive as had been feared in CHC circles. It had been widely expected that the DHSS and the regional health authorities would substantially reduce the number of health districts across the country, and that the number of community health councils would diminish in accordance with this change. Neither outcome in practice emerged.

The DHSS took the opportunity to recognise the growth of certain areas of the country and to create new health districts based on Milton Keynes, Skelmersdale and Huntingdon, and with them, new CHCs to represent the public interest in those localities. Major health district realignments took place in London, and in the Trent and South Western regions, resulting in the merger of several districts and their respective CHCs. Trent RHA took the most radical steps, condensing the cities of Sheffield and Nottingham and the county of Leicestershire to one single district each, and reducing the number of districts in Derbyshire to two, with a resulting loss of five CHCs in the region.

This measure of realignment had been anticipated on a broader scale across the country, notably in Manchester and Liverpool, where there was much speculation at the time about the likely creation of a single district and a single CHC for each of the cities. In the end, it was only the East Midlands and South Yorkshire which were affected. In the South Western region, the Somerset health districts were merged, and a countywide CHC created to match the new authority. Bristol and Weston-super-Mare were merged into one district, but the CHCs were permitted to remain for the time being.

In London, the central (teaching) districts were all realigned, bringing about mergers in Lewisham and Southwark; in Merton and Sutton; in Hammersmith, and in Camden and Westminster. Some adjustments also took place at the fringes of Greater London, where Barking and Havering CHCs on the eastern extreme were combined, as were Barnet/Finchley and Edgware/Hendon in the north west, and Hounslow and North Surrey at the most westerly point.

In the Northern region, the two small CHCs in southern Cumbria were merged to form South Cumbria, based at Kendal, while the Mersey region took a similar step with the Wirral CHCs, locating the new Wirral CHC in the vicinity of the recently completed Arrowe Park hospital. All in all however, the jigsaw was only marginally changed, and the number of CHCs in England reduced by some 5% in the aftermath of April 1982.

Although further realignments of approximately similar impact were to take place later in London, Leeds, the Northern region and the South West (at Bristol and in Gloucestershire) the number of CHCs that survived until 2003 – at 184 in England and 19 in Wales – was only around 10% fewer than those existing at the beginning of 1982.

By August 1983, Tony Smythe had taken over from me as Director of the association. I had known Tony, who first made his name in the 1960s as Director of the National

Council for Civil Liberties and later enjoyed much success as Director of MIND, for many years, and greatly admired him as a standard bearer for disadvantaged people. CHCs came into existence at a period which was notable for its powerful campaigners in the arena of social justice as much as it was for the development of consumerism. It was the time when people such as Des Wilson were putting homelessness into the public conscience; Alf Morris and (Baroness) Sue Masham had persuaded parliament to take its first, hesitant, legislative steps to correct the official neglect of disabled people; Brian Rix had taken the helm of MENCAP, and Germaine Greer and Erin Pizzey were stamping women's issues indelibly on the national consciousness. They had a cause. They were committed and forceful, and a decade of unprecedented change in outlook and attitudes had inevitably precipitated the emergence of people of this stamp, including many I have not mentioned, at about the same time. I knew quite a number of them, and without any disrespect to those concerned or their achievements I have to say that in my estimation, Tony was the *non pareil*.

Courageous, determined and utterly independent in his way of thinking and acting, he never lost sight of his objectives and beliefs, and never compromised them. For Tony, it was the cause that counted, and in everything he attempted, it was the advancement of the cause that dictated his actions and drove him on. He was never to my knowledge interested in personal advancement, and he had an almost messianic view of himself and his talents as a part of the means by which greater objectives could be achieved.

I too had an absolute personal commitment to CHCs and the conception of popular empowerment that I saw as implicit in them. Yet I was also convinced of the necessity for a periodic infusion of new thinking and new commitment into their organisation, to keep them fresh and adventurous, and to prevent them becoming stale or bureaucratic. For this reason, I was anxious to hand over the reins of ACHCEW to a completely different type of person before I, or the association, became too set in our ways. So, when I began to feel, after the 1982 reorganisation, that we had come to the end of the second (post-"Patients First") phase in the life of CHCs, I also began to feel that it was time for me to put this conviction into effect. Being a fan of Tony Smythe, I was keen that he should show an interest, and delighted when he decided to put his name forward, and was selected as my successor.

I knew Tony well enough to be aware that the interaction of his personality with the corporate personality of ACHCEW, and more broadly, with the corporate personality of some two hundred CHCs, would at times be colourful – or even pyrotechnic – but I have never found creative tension either unpleasant or unproductive, and was sure that Tony's commitment and sincerity would win friends once he had settled in.

This did not work out completely as planned. People in CHCs – members and chief officers alike – knew his reputation and track record, and many took the view, either that his position was too radical for an organisation that however belligerent, was naturally conservative in its attitude to its responsibilities; or that as a strong and opinionated person he would attempt to impose his control on the entire organisation, thereby extending the influence of ACHCEW unacceptably and compromising the independence of its membership. The result was that the chemistry never really worked, and Tony's period as director turned out to be relatively short.

John Austin, who was chairman of ACHCEW when he was appointed, said: "I was a very great admirer of Tony Smythe as Director of MIND, as a champion of the underprivileged, the depressed, the disadvantaged; but I think he had difficulty in being the chief executive officer of a collegiate organisation. Some people felt that in one sense he was bigger than the organisation. He was a great campaigner, and he achieved enormous things when he was at MIND, but ACHCEW was a different sort of animal. It was a democratic organisation with a standing committee you had to take with you, and a constantly vigilant membership, assertive of its own independence and autonomy, and unwilling to relinquish any part of it to any individual or group, however able or charismatic."

Whatever else might be said about him, Tony was one of the great campaigners of the later twentieth century, and community health councils were privileged to have him for a time among their number. It was with great sorrow that I learned of his early death in 2004.

New thinking was certainly called for at the time Tony Smythe became secretary of the association, but it was not the kind that I had envisaged. The withdrawal of government funding from *CHC News* was an act of further-reaching impact than even ministers might have imagined. It not only deprived CHCs of their journal and information service; it also deprived ACHCEW of the contribution *CHC News* made to its overhead costs.

The *CHC News* share of office accommodation; of heating and lighting; telephone costs, and common services in general, could no longer be met from DHSS payments received and became a charge on ACHCEW, which had to be paid for out of its subscription income. In the starkest terms, the fixed costs – with the important exception of salaries – remained, and so did the variables. What had gone was the means of meeting them. The result was obvious, and predictable. The association got into financial difficulties which could only be resolved by drastic economies and by increasing its charges to CHCs.

Thus, almost before Tony Smythe had taken his seat in the ACHCEW office, he and it were plunged into an agony of argument, recrimination and uncertainty which lasted for more than twelve months and threatened to destroy the network of mutual co-operation and confidence between

CHCs and their association that had been painstakingly (and sometimes painfully), built up over the preceding seven years.

It involved no less than three general meetings during 1984: two of them ad-hoc Saturday meetings at the Royal Commonwealth Society in London, on 25 February and 29 September, and the AGM, also in London, at the City University on 7/8 June. Characteristic of all these meetings were motions of no confidence in the officers of ACHCEW, long and contentious reports detailing the grim and expensive options available for resolving the crisis, and threats from member CHCs of withdrawal if the solutions offered were not to their satisfaction or proved too costly.

It was the February meeting which voted "by a large majority" that *CHC News* should cease publication and should be wound up as soon as it could be arranged. The meeting further decided that a Committee of Inquiry should be formed to consider and make proposals concerning (a) the future staffing of ACHCEW and its financial basis, with particular reference to future subscription levels; (b) the role and functions of the standing committee, officers and staff of the association, and (c) any other relevant issues; consulting, and taking account of the views of member CHCs before preparing its report, which should be presented to the AGM in the coming June.

In the earliest days of ACHCEW, I had realised that a two-person office was too small to carry out all the functions expected of it, and to involve itself in complex matters such as payroll and VAT. I had therefore negotiated with the North East Thames Regional Health Authority, which handled the payroll for the seventeen CHCs in the region, that it take on the Association's payroll work as well, which would entail a very small administrative input on the part of the RHA, and spare us the quite major accounting and audit effort it would require if we were to institute our own payroll system. ACHCEW made a monthly payment to the RHA covering the salaries, national insurance and superannuation of its staff, and the RHA did the rest. No charge was made for this service, since the RHA calculated that the process of billing it to ACHCEW would cost it more than the service itself.

Similarly, I had prepared a case for the Customs and Excise for the exemption of the association from VAT liability, and had attended a meeting at their headquarters close to the Tower of London, where this position was hammered out and agreed. I was very proud of these two agreements, which I knew had greatly eased our administrative pathway during the formative stage.

The minutes of the Special General Meeting on 25 February show that the Vice-Chairman had reported that "ACHCEW had not gone bankrupt only because a major creditor, the N.E. Thames RHA, had not pressed for payment for three months' salaries." My initiative was still benefitting the association, even if in a way that I had not foreseen. At the same time, a further example of generosity to community health councils on the part of a RHA had been uncovered.

Reviewing the year (1984/85) at the AGM a year later, the Treasurer was to report that one of the headaches of the year from his point of view was notification from Customs and Excise that the association would now have to register for VAT. The outcome of his negotiations was less successful than my earlier effort, but times had changed and ACHCEW by now was dealing in quite substantial sums as a conference organiser. Happily, a compromise position was possible, and liability for VAT was limited to transactions relating to the Annual General Meetings. This remained the situation until the association was dissolved in 2003.

The report of the Committee of Inquiry was the predominant component of the 1984 AGM, occupying all or part of every plenary session except the third (Thursday evening), when the guest speakers addressed the meeting, and NHS-related motions from CHCs were debated. The standing committee also met during the lunch interval on the Friday to review the position as it stood at the time. A number of decisions were finally taken, involving a reduction in the number of standing committee members; an immediate move from the offices in Euston Road to less costly premises elsewhere, and a further special meeting being called to approve an amended constitution, financial and operational standing orders for ACHCEW, and to be held as quickly as possible after the AGM. Dissolution of the association was to be on the same agenda as a possible outcome. This meeting took place on 29 September 1984.

There were some positive indicators for the standing committee to bring to the third meeting. ACHCEW had by this time obtained a DHSS grant of £27,500 to cover its deficit, and had also moved to different, less expensive premises. The problem of accommodation was not solved, but the new office was on a two-year licence, giving some breathing space in which to find a permanent home.

These developments did little to stifle debate on the substantive issues of whether or not the association should continue in existence or should be wound up, and what form it should take if it were to remain. Every recommendation from the platform was vigorously argued for and against, as were each of the constitutional amendments once the principal decision was taken. By the end of the afternoon, the future shape of ACHCEW had been engineered and a budget for 1985/86 agreed. The delegates of the 152 CHCs which had taken part were able to return to their districts in the knowledge that for the time being, the internal blood-letting was over, and that in the words of chairman John Butler: "ACHCEW should continue on the basis of the motions [agreed], and should get on with its job."

The coda to this lengthy piece was played at the ACHCEW AGM at Nottingham in July 1985. John Butler was able to inform those present that a grant of £20,000 from the DHSS had enabled the association to employ an information officer, with the possibility of a further £20–27,000 in 1986/87. Ministerial guest speaker John Patten later underlined the new rights given to CHCs, in relation to Family Practitioner Committees and announced a further extension, giving them a consultative role on entry to the pharmaceutical lists of FPCs.

Tony Smythe made two important statements in the context of the Annual Report, telling delegates first that he had built up a mailing list of helpful MPs, the use of which he intended to develop in the future. Resolutions of the meeting would be sent to them, and his aim was to encourage them to become active in representing the policies and concerns of CHCs to government. Towards the end of his presentation, he stated that CHCs had to be alerted to issues with a health component which did not directly emanate from the DHSS or the NHS hierarchy. Instancing the bill to deregulate bus services as an example, he added that concerted action at a national level through ACHCEW was vital if the interests of NHS patients were to be protected. This reassertion of the national role of the association and its member CHCs was received by the meeting without any dissent.

Tony made one further significant observation while motions from CHCs were being debated during the final session of the meeting. Commenting on a proposal that a meeting with the Secretary of State (Norman Fowler) should be sought before the parliamentary summer recess, he remarked that as the debate was being held on 12 July, it would in any case be difficult within the time frame available, but it was more likely to be impossible in view of Mr Fowler's apparent reluctance to have any contact with the association.

Throughout the lifetime of CHCs, Norman Fowler was perhaps the least accessible Secretary of State. I only met him twice, once at a public function while I was secretary of ACHCEW and once some years later when he was Secretary of State for Employment and I came to London to receive an award on behalf of the Shetland Islands Council. I didn't really know him at all, and on both occasions found it hard to exchange conversation with him. He certainly was not highly communicative, and I am tempted to say that I never received a letter from the DHSS under his personal signature. At any rate, I have very little recollection of doing so, and when I wrote to him to tell him about this book and to ask for his own reflections on CHCs, I received an acknowledgement from his office at the House of Lords, but never heard any more.

By 1986 the mood among CHCs was more optimistic, largely on account of the much improved financial situation of ACHCEW (for which Mr Fowler may well deserve gratitude), and the renewed availability to them of a regular printed newsletter and an information service. The notes made by an anonymous delegate to the ACHCEW AGM in Canterbury spoke of a debate on a document entitled "The Future Role and Structure of CHCs" prepared for the meeting by a working group, which was going to be highly influential in the run up to the 1987 general election, and should be sent to all the political parties to elicit their response to it. There was also a comment on the inter-sessional workshops, which the writer found "get better and better... All those attending remarked on the exceptionally high quality of the workshops", to which was added that it "was felt to be a very successful [meeting] from which [participants] could go back to their CHCs with plenty to think about and a great deal to do". If this opinion was typical, then the feeling in the country at this time was very much more positive than it had been the previous year, and in all probability at any time since the summer of 1979.

From her vantage point in the shadow of Portchester castle, Margaret Lovell was also able to see a growth in confidence among the members and staff of CHCs in the later 1980s. She remembered that collectively they appeared to become much stronger, and began to integrate the business of campaigning nationally for policy and funding improvements with their vision of a more effective and beneficial service for patients and users of the NHS in their localities. Members were becoming more self-confident in their representative role, while Wessex RHA and the local district health authority were going some way towards reinforcing this sense of increasing competence by acknowledging the legitimacy of the CHC and giving respect to its pronouncements.

The working patterns of the CHC were becoming more precise, in that members had begun to put a collective finger on areas in which local health services were most in need of scrutiny and targeting their work accordingly. The result of this (at least in Portsmouth and South East Hampshire) was that their vision shifted from acute hospital settings to settle more decisively than hitherto on mental health issues and learning difficulties. Margaret recalled that her members also drew strength from the work of other CHCs in these areas of provision as the movement from institutional to community care gathered momentum, and alongside the lifestyle improvements achieved by many former institutional patients, certain less beneficial side effects of change began to be perceived.

Many CHCs had pointed out from the start that community care was not a low-cost alternative, and that some new-style residential care facilities would become a necessity. They had argued their case persuasively, but in the prevailing climate of financial stringency, the official response had been more in terms of the 'old' money to be saved than the 'new' money needing to be spent. In Margaret Lovell's opinion, speaking up knowledgeably and persistently for the less articulate members of society was one of the most powerful forces for good exercised by CHCs in every part of the country at the time.

It was equally her recollection that new chief officers being appointed to CHCs at this stage were coming more frequently from voluntary organisations such as campaigning groups and councils of voluntary service, and in general from non-NHS sources rather than the health service. This may have been because a certain sum of government money was at the time in circulation supporting short term contract or project work in the voluntary sector, and because people who had benefitted from this type of work were keen to find more permanent employment in a comparable field and were thus attracted to CHC opportunities. Certainly at the time there were less NHS employees having to reapply for their own jobs or simply looking for a way out, and the work was less attractive to those taking early retirement than it had been ten years earlier, since it was more demanding than it had seemed in 1974 and no longer relatively so well paid.

This all meant that new recruits to CHCs were less likely to be imbued with health service culture and preconceptions, and more likely to see things from the council's viewpoint, which clearly promised beneficial results for the CHC. It was, of course, open to CHCs to make use of short-term or project grants and thereby enlarge their working capacity, sometimes in collaboration with, or with some financial or other input from the health authorities themselves. These and other opportunities were spotted by enterprising councils and chief officers, who were able to increase the amount of work they did as a result.

To complete the picture, it appeared to Margaret Lovell that NHS managers seemed to have come to the conclusion that there was some advantage in notifying CHCs about intended service changes of all kinds and enabling the position of both bodies relative to the changes to be mutually understood prior to formal consultation. Many NHS clinicians, in her experience, still preferred to stay at arm's length, and were reluctant to share information or work in collaboration with CHCs. This, of course, was about the time when Jean Robinson was revolutionising the General Medical Council.

Jean Robinson was appointed to the GMC in 1979 and served for fourteen years as a lay member. She sat on the Professional Conduct Committee, and her monograph "A Patient Voice at the GMC" was published in 1988. She was a member of Oxfordshire CHC, having been appointed by Oxford RHA in 1974. When she completed her term of office, she was repeatedly co-opted to membership for a further twenty-three years. Jean is very proud of her unbroken service to the CHC from inception to dissolution.

The General Medical Council has been in existence since 1838, and was set up by statute, with the purpose of regulating the medical profession and protecting patients against unprofessional or incompetent doctors. Its costs have traditionally been met from the registration fees paid by doctors. It is not therefore a charge on the NHS or the Department of Health, and its unique source of funding, coupled with its historic composition, have caused many doctors to regard it as a body that exists for their benefit and that of their profession. This misconception has been fuelled over the years by procedures and practices described in the Harold Shipman inquiry report as "focussed too much on the interests of doctors", which coloured and animated Jean Robinson's impressions, as will now be seen.

Jean was not in any way intimidated when she first arrived at the GMC, having served for some years prior to 1974 on the Oxford regional health board, and as the wife of a fellow of Magdalen, having attended numerous university functions, both formal and informal. She described it as "very gentlemanly, smooth, civilised and welcoming", with a totally male ethos, particularly in terms of its behavioural expectations.

She had been appointed by the Privy Council, through the DHSS, having been nominated by ACHCEW, and she was extremely glad to have the community health council network behind her, since it gave her a constituency to consult, and credibility in debate. CHCs did not feature prominently among the GMC's preoccupations, which were broadly centred on the regulation of the profession, medical education and ethics; they were generally accepted by the GMC as part of the NHS structure. But as a member, Jean Robinson was able to interact with her constituency and speak with a level of authority that would not have been possible had she originated from a different source (see also footnote, Appendix 2).

The most obvious feature of the Council was the overwhelming majority of doctors among its membership. The GMC had been reorganised by the 1978 Medical Act to comprise fifty doctors elected by the profession, thirty-four members appointed by the Royal Colleges and the universities (presumably also predominantly doctors), and nine appointed by the Crown, of whom seven were lay members. Its obligation under the Medical Act, as I have explained above, was to regulate the medical profession in the interests of the nation. This created an immediate conflict of interest, since a clear majority of members had been elected by other doctors to represent their interests. Jean was conscious of this, and its corollary, that their first priority as members was to safeguard the right of the medical profession to regulate itself.

In defence of this position, they were not prepared to concede an issue of principle unless they had no alternative, and even then, would do so only to the minimum extent necessary to maintain their professional hegemony. They traded favours (e.g. the chairmanship of a committee) when necessary to buy off dissent within the ranks, or as a hedge against adverse publicity or shifts of opinion. In this way the GMC was a demonstration of medical politics, skilfully and urbanely handled but clinically effective.

What Jean Robinson found changed the behaviour of committees was the presence of women. The elected members of the GMC in most instances were male, and there were very few women, even among those elected by the profession. "Sometimes" she told me "I would be the only female member of a Professional Conduct Committee dealing with a gynaecology case, or an obstetric case, or a sexual abuse case. What made a difference was not the other lay members, but having other women because [whether medical or not], women would see things from the individual's point of view."

This point is interesting for two reasons; first, because of the perception she identified as common to the women, and second, because there is no suggestion of any community of feeling between the lay members. The lay members used to have a pre-meeting in the morning before the full council meeting in the afternoon, possibly to reach an agreed view on some of the business, or possibly to tease out the lay-person's issues in the council agenda. According to Jean "although the lay members weren't radical, we were always very matey" but evidently on the questions raised by allegations of serious professional misconduct, they were split according to gender.

On occasions she found the entire body of lay members lined up against her. Any member of the GMC could table a resolution for a council meeting, though not many chose to do so. Jean was an exception ("I think I was the only one who ever did"), and put resolutions down when she felt an issue should be debated. On some, she might not get a majority vote; on others, she might not even get a seconder, but there was a permanent record in the minutes of the council showing that the resolution had been moved. On one occasion only, when the entire council was opposed to the resolution she intended to propose, and under pressure from all quarters, medical and lay, did Jean Robinson decide to withdraw it. She later realised that she should have remained firm, and has always regretted that she did not do so.

Her monograph on the GMC, subtitled "A lay member's view of the General Medical Council" explains how the

GMC worked in 1988, how complaints against doctors came to be made, and the sifting process which preceded a hearing and ensured that the number of complaints considered by the Council was a very small proportion of those made. She commented on the shortcomings of the GMC procedures, and the many pitfalls faced by complainants or their relatives.

She discussed the appropriateness of "serious professional misconduct" (the only grounds on which a complaint could be made to the GMC); the definition of "serious" and the difficulty of making a charge of this nature stick; and the alternatives of "professional misconduct" and "unacceptable conduct" which might have enabled more complaints to be heard, and more of them to be successful. She also described the standard NHS procedures for complaints against GPs and hospital doctors as they were at the time, remarking on the difficulty faced by complainants under each of them in obtaining satisfaction. She used case studies to illustrate her main argument and to show just how well the system protected doctors from the consequences of their actions or failures to act. "A Patient Voice" is a genuinely instructive book, and evidence, one would suppose, for an overhaul of the system.

Yet today, so many years later, after everything that has come to light meanwhile, the most conspicuous activity of the GMC has yet to be decisively altered. While it has been deeply involved in the debate as to what a medical practitioner should be, and what standards of behaviour and competence should be expected; while it has introduced new procedures for registration and revalidation, and been a central party to the modernisation of both undergraduate and postgraduate medical education and training in this country, it is not yet clear whether the GMC has put its house in order so far as its complaints machinery is concerned, and in the wake of the Shipman inquiry report its very existence is being challenged.

It has already lost some of its autonomy. The Council for Healthcare Regulatory Excellence (CHRE) was set up in 2003 to keep an eye on the performance of regulating bodies including the GMC, which has recently separated its professional conduct (now renamed Fitness to Practise) function from the council itself. In November 2004 it overhauled its initial sifting procedures to make them more open and consistent. Fitness to Practice panels are now the bodies which investigate complaints, and no council members may sit on them. The composition of the council has also been changed, so that lay members now constitute forty per cent of the total membership.

Many of Jean Robinson's observations have a prophetic ring about them. At several points she referred to the GMC's attitude to its work, remarking in this context that what parliament has given in the form of legislative authority, parliament is able to take away. Certainly significant changes have been called for in recent years, and it remains to be seen whether parliament will be satisfied with the results of the changes outlined above.

Despite efforts made in both houses more than twenty years ago, the only grounds for complaints to the GMC are still "serious professional misconduct", and according to *Which?* health reports (January 2005) "some recent GMC decisions seem surprisingly lenient towards doctors... The GMC has yet to announce any changes to its guidance about what constitutes serious misconduct or when particular penalties should apply. It is due to consult on new guidance about sanctions this month. We shall be [responding to] the consultation, to ensure the guidance works to protect patients." The Shipman inquiry report is meanwhile recommending that if the new processes prove unsuccessful within the next few years, the GMC should pass responsibility for the final stage of Fitness to Practise investigations to an independent body.

In her introduction to "A Patient Voice", Jean Robinson wrote "I have learned things about the GMC which could not easily be discovered by a member of the public... I have found it increasingly hard to reconcile the collective behaviour of the profession with the individual care, kindness and decency of the many doctors I know. I want to share this knowledge with others, so that those who try to lodge complaints with the GMC will be better informed, so that public debate will be stimulated, and so that the medical profession will know more about what is being done in their name." One of the main targets for this knowledge was her CHC constituency, and the book was circulated to CHCs so that they would have the information the public lacked, and would be able to guide complainants and their advisers effectively. It is an open question even now whether the implications of 'what is being done in their name' have yet dawned on the medical profession as a whole.

Community health councils are no longer present to see what finally emerges from these upheavals, and Jean Robinson's final comment to me after we had talked was this sad reflection: "the establishment of CHCs in 1973 was a typically British (or maybe English?) piece of improvisation – an unfinished idea put together into as coherent a shape as was possible – which worked far better than anyone involved had a right to expect. Their most important asset was the national network, and the value of its accumulated knowledge was incalculable. This [knowledge] is the most tragic victim of abolition." Many of those in a position to know would no doubt agree.

But at the time she wrote "A Patient Voice" community health councils appeared to be flourishing. They were not under attack; they had been given new functions, and by all accounts greater respect from the health service. They were shortly to benefit from an increase in resources, giving them the ability to take on additional staff and a more ambitious workload, and their chief officers were about to be advanced in status. Toby Harris was presiding over a larger-scale ACHCEW than his predecessors had known, and Wyn Pockett was a highly experienced and knowledgeable association chair, approaching her third year of office. From every direction the barometer looked Set Fair.

In the days of sail, ships leaving temperate latitudes to cross the equator in either direction would at a certain point leave the strong westerly winds of the north or south and the sub-tropical trade winds behind them, entering an equatorial region of calms, sudden storms and unpredictable winds, which if they were unlucky, could repeatedly put them in danger or leave them becalmed for a long time. This region of the ocean was known to sailors as the doldrums. As they approached the half-way point in their lives, CHCs were entering the curious world of the post-Thatcher-pre-Blair period of British politics: their own doldrums, in which they were to lie for several years reacting to apparently endless changes in the structure and management of the NHS, and trying persistently but without very much success to redefine themselves in terms of the performance-driven and competitive ethos of the 1990s.

Chapter Six

Snap Judgments and Insight

"CHCs are not uniformly effective; many are mediocre; and in some the legitimate activity of critical comment on the district's or FPC's health care provision shades into direct political action against the policies of the government of the day."

("The Role of CHCs", Department of Health, November 1989)

While community health councils were furling up their sails to wait for a favourable wind, this powerful statement was being written somewhere in the DoH using the rhetoric of the Patrick Jenkin period, and making assertions about them which were clearly part of the received wisdom between the writer and his intended readers, and therefore required no substantiation.

How far this was part of the perception of CHCs at the time (even if less aggressively expressed) is demonstrated by a paper prepared by Christine Hogg at about the same time, where she states that in 1974 the newborn CHCs "were left to work out their own priorities and ways of relating to health authorities. The broad scope of CHC responsibilities and the limited resources led to *wide variations between CHCs* all over the country." In a project proposal to ACHCEW in June 1990, her first premise was "It is generally accepted that community health councils need to be reformed..." and as background she adds: "The lack of guidance from the beginning has resulted in *enormous variability* in the services offered by individual CHCs to the public and to NHS managers." This comment is quoted from her 1986 paper "The public and the NHS".

Christine Hogg is certainly consistent in her opinions. But she is also a staunch supporter of CHCs and the broader concepts of patient and community involvement. The aim of the project she was promoting was to produce recommendations on a framework for developing user representation in the NHS in the long term, and to set standards and methods of making user representation in local communities more effective: her purpose was to strengthen the one by grounding it firmly in the other.

In November 2003, just before CHCs were disbanded, I spoke to Christine to open up the issue of variability with her. She told me that she didn't believe it was the fault of the councils themselves. She considered that they had been designed without any standards, so that there was no way performance could be objectively monitored. She was sure that the responsibility for this lay with the government, but that if ACHCEW had had the courage to research and promulgate standards for CHCs during the late 1980s or early 1990s the situation could have been saved. The reason why she deplored Alan Milburn's abrupt decision to abolish them was that "there is so much variability in all health services: GPs and hospitals are all very variable, not to mention the primary care trusts. But we don't say that's a reason for abolishing them. We say it's a reason for regulation and standard setting. But there was no will in government to do something sensible like that, although they could have done it."

I put it to Christine that her view on variability is widely shared, but that it is very difficult to draw out what qualities constitute a good CHC or a bad one. She replied that by definition some good CHCs would be unpopular with NHS managers, since while an able manager would welcome the stimulus of a good CHC, less gifted managers would not. She thought that most CHCs were better in some areas than others, with the result that a CHC could, for example, be really good in terms of user involvement and public participation, but offer a poor service to complainants. Another CHC might spend much of its time on complaints, and win praise for its efforts from the individuals concerned, while being seen as useless by those interested in community involvement. With no clear standards or accountability, who could say that one is right and the other wrong? But they obviously differ greatly in what they do.

She offered some objective quality criteria: how thorough they were in reaching conclusions; how conscientiously they did their research; the degree to which they spoke on behalf of local people; how faithfully they reflected local opinion and how far they were speaking for themselves.

Christine again commented that at the key time CHCs lacked powerful and positive promotion at the national level. She believed that Donna Covey had tried to lead from the front. In commissioning Will Hutton's report and establishing an all-party group of MPs with an interest in CHCs, she was trying to put them centre stage and popularise their cause, but failed because Alan Milburn decided to kill them without any warning; consultation, or any real understanding.

Christine Hogg is the only person who has attempted to define for me her criteria for a 'good' CHC, or to explain what she meant by 'variable'. In all other cases, the charge of variability has been unsubstantiated by any instances, and when pressed, people have generally replied to the effect that the CHCs they had dealt with personally were reasonable. If anyone had said to me (for example) "West Bedfordshire CHC is no good, because it never takes any action that will upset the DHA, and the chief officer plays golf every Thursday afternoon with one of the consultants; or Wearside CHC is 'mediocre', because it is constantly at loggerheads with its neighbouring CHCs and prefers to keep itself to itself rather than making any effort at co-operation with them; or that Eastville and Ashton CHC is unacceptable because it is always conducting raucous campaigns in support of its inner-city communities, and its far-left ideology keeps it at odds with the DHA, and sometimes with the RHA as well", I should have understood what they meant. These characteristics, if slightly extreme, are those which generally seem to find disfavour.

Yet even if it were possible to unearth such insufferable CHCs, it may be the case that West Bedfordshire produce the most magnificent and influential annual reports and preside over a well and thoughtfully provided health district; that the intellectual content of Wearside's extensively researched and closely argued council papers is unsurpassed, and that Eastville and Ashton is an iconic body in the central city, where its roots in the community and commitment to minority health issues are legendary. It is not so easy to judge community-based organisations as at first sight it might seem.

The same DoH paper was able to say to ministers that the general managers of the RHAs were dubious about extending the role of CHCs on the grounds that managers and clinicians would meet any such proposals with hostility. Not surprisingly, its content alarmed Toby Harris, who at once released it to all the CHCs in England and Wales, so that nobody should be left unaware. It was not as if CHCs intended to arouse hostility: in her simultaneous paper, Christine Hogg was urging collaborative working with DHAs on databases and survey work, and with voluntary and local community bodies in advice and advocacy, bearing in mind the community focus of the CHC and the client group orientation of many voluntary groups. Reminding CHCs that the health service was still less than adequately responsive to its users and that its need for an 'external examiner' was as great then as in 1974, she presented her own eight-point plan for CHCs in the following terms:

1) CHCs need to be clearly independent of the NHS authorities. Some body other than regional health authorities should be designated as the establishing and resourcing authority.

2) CHC activities should be reviewed and reassessed, and they should focus more on the role of independent community advocate.

3) Minimum performance standards need to be established, with provision for independent review and monitoring.

4) Innovative means must be found to make CHCs accountable to their community. All CHCs need to set up mechanisms to report back to their communities.

5) The statutory duties of CHCs have increased, and so has the number of enquiries and complaints. Resources provided should be correspondingly expanded.

6) Increased investment in member and staff training and information is needed to improve joint working and effectiveness.

7) More research into consumer groups and representational techniques is necessary to enable new ways of involving NHS users and engaging the public in policy and planning.

8) Government and health service managers must work with CHCs to develop a future role and to provide the resources to underwrite effective and independent user representation.

This was the call that paved the way for a seven-year search for the holy grail of workable performance standards. I am in no doubt that the feeling existed among many CHC members and chief officers that "something needed to be done" to counteract the constant charge of variability laid at the door of CHCs (but not any other bodies, even though a number of health authorities had their knuckles rapped from time to time) which proved impossible to counter conclusively. Christine Hogg put down on paper what many others expressed in debate or in aspiration, and the world of CHCs responded.

The Royal College of Nursing had, at about the same time, recommended to the Department that CHCs should be given independence from all health authorities, and as we have seen, some of the more lateral thinkers in CHCs were taking a similar view. ACHCEW very quickly picked up and pursued this theme in its own representations. But with a Department that was plainly not well disposed to CHCs where it mattered, this far from impossible or unreasonable proposal was unlikely to make much ground. By the latter part of 1990 it had been made completely clear that the official objective was, if anything, to clip the wings of CHCs and reduce their scope, using the NHS and Community Care Act, and the introduction of self-governing Trusts and fundholding GPs as its rationale for doing so.

What may puzzle the reader is how it happened that CHCs and ACHCEW, which were in close, or at least regular touch with ministers, MPs and civil servants, were apparently unaware of the vein of hostility running through the Department and the confidence with which it could be expressed to ministers. The shock of discovery is evident in Toby Harris's letter to CHCs of 19 February 1990, which is written defensively, and is as much a call for help as an item of information. Perhaps there was a measure of complacency (or at least of relief) – to continue the sea-going metaphor – at having got into clear water after a stormy ride, that led them momentarily to take their eye off the horizon, and they were caught out. I have advised elsewhere against underestimating the tenacity of your opponents, and it may well be that the forked-tongue of civil servants and the RHAs had lulled them into an incautious sense of security. Or

161

perhaps they simply were just tired of seeming paranoid, but it is certain that the underlying threat had not evaporated.

Obviously hindsight is a more comfortable viewpoint than the heat of the battle, but I believe that experience should have taught those concerned at the time to remain vigilant, and not to allow themselves to relax when things appeared to be going well. It is interesting to recall that Kenneth Clarke was Secretary of State at the time. His comments to me (Appendix Two) suggest that the civil servants who wrote the paper that triggered off Toby's letter were relaxed enough with their minister to speak in such an unrestrained way.

On the positive side, the same Regional General Managers who were perturbed by the possibility of the role of CHCs being extended were asked to look into the resourcing of CHCs with a view to making them more effective in what they did. It is no secret that this led to additional staff and office facilities becoming available; that regional advisers or co-ordinators of CHCs were appointed, and that regional groupings were given official recognition, with offices and staff of their own. Secretaries, as we have seen, became Chief Officers, and retained that status until the end of 2003.

Meanwhile, the energies of CHCs and their association were once again given over during the following twelve months to clawing back some of the ground that had been taken away from them, and it is fair to say that their efforts were quite successful. The main ministerial target for their arguments and the source of the concessions they obtained was Stephen Dorrell, who at the time was Parliamentary Secretary in the DoH; who attended the association AGM in York in July 1991, and the standing committee in December that year. Beyond this, Mr Dorrell was responsible for the instructions issued to health authorities at all levels in Executive Letter EL(92)11 in March 1992 concerning co-operation with CHCs, to which I shall return presently.

In his speech at York, Mr Dorrell said: "Those who manage public services must remember to whom they are responsible. They should be judged, not by their peers, but by their customers – the community who pay their salaries." He went on to say that the new purchasing function of district health authorities "will bring the DHA and the CHC much closer together... DHA and CHC must work to empower the patient." Stephen Dorrell almost certainly found a responsive chord among his audience, when in his concluding passage he remarked: "I expect CHCs to say that resources are inadequate to carry out their functions – I would be foolish to think otherwise. What I would not expect is for that argument to be used as an excuse for not performing as well as CHCs are able to; I would like to see CHCs ensuring that they make optimum use of what I agree are limited resources."

In the setting of a conference, this could sound as if the minister was sympathetic to CHCs' resource aspirations. It could sound as if he was keen that they should make a good showing in collaboration with their DHAs, and in general encouraging. But in fact it was an oracular statement: he did not say he would do anything about the resources available, neither did he imply anything except that he didn't want CHCs whingeing about money or staff; he just wanted them to get on with the job. Eight months later, by means of EL(92)11, the NHS Executive confirmed his instruction to RHAs to "ensure that CHCs are properly resourced and... adequate arrangements are made for the development of CHC staff."

Toby Harris told me that the visit Stephen Dorrell paid to the standing committee of ACHCEW was constructive, and in the context of what happened next it is impossible to argue with his assessment. Mr Dorrell spoke quite briefly to the meeting, using the opportunity to explain his conception of the significance of the provider/purchaser split in NHS structures and the role available to CHCs as the user's representative in keeping the local purchasers (DHAs) in line with the public interest. He answered a variety of questions before leaving, and agreed to meet the officers of ACHCEW six weeks later. Two weeks after the second meeting, he sent a letter to the chairmen of regional and district health authorities advising them of his wishes regarding their relationships with CHCs. Some three weeks later, letter EL(92)11 spelled out the same message to the authorities in the form of instructions. This, as the first ever ministerial directive of its kind must have been one of the most welcome letters received by CHCs during their entire twenty-nine years. Because of its significance, the complete text of the operative paragraphs is reproduced below:

"1. Stephen Dorrell, Parliamentary Under Secretary of State, wrote to Regional and District Health Authority Chairmen on 14 February (ML(92)1) about the role of CHCs. I am writing to draw attention to the contents of his letter from a management standpoint.

"2. DHAs should:
- **Involve CHCs in the purchasing process.** DHAs should agree locally with CHCs how they should contribute to the assessment of relative priorities, development of quality standards, target setting and monitoring arrangements;
- **Consider the scope for joint initiatives with CHCs**. These could include CHCs facilitating a dialogue with local people and helping to convey information to them, as suggested in the NHSME paper "Local Voices".
- **Ensure CHCs have access to information** such as DHA contracts with providers, purchasing plans, data about local health needs and services. DHAs should normally hold GP Fund Holders' contracts and should make these available to CHCs (anonymised to protect patient confidentiality).

"3. These principles are also applicable to FHSAs (Family Health Service Authorities, the name then in use for the former Family Practitioner Committees), who should inform and seek CHCs' views about FSHA planning intentions.

"4. Regions should ensure that CHCs are properly resourced and that adequate arrangements are made for the development of CHC staff. They should ensure that DHAs and FHSAs are taking action as outlined above."

This is a quite remarkable turn-round from November 1990, when letter EL(90)185 put into effect the constrictions that had made ACHCEW so anxious at the beginning of the year and precipitated a briefing note from Toby Harris to MPs to alert them to the effect of the changes. ACHCEW Chair Rita Lewis, and Toby could feel justified in congratulating each other on "a very good year".

The search for performance standards for CHCs went on, at both regional and national level, and undoubtedly it was a matter of priority for the many CHCs which were keen to clear themselves of the stigma of mediocrity. Despite its preoccupation with recovering lost ground, ACHCEW found time in 1991 to produce a paper on the core activities of CHCs, offering a kind of template against which they could define their own objectives, establish targets, and construct a work programme aimed at their achievement.

In conversation with me, Beryl Furr and Barrie Taylor described their work on peer group assessment, and this was published for the benefit of CHCs in 1992 under the title "Self Reviews in Community Health Councils". In the same year, the Yorkshire Regional Group of CHCs took part in a regional exercise that produced a number of performance standards for CHCs under the headings of Accessibility (location, opening hours, signage, welcome, space and privacy, facilities offered to the public at meetings); Information (speed and clarity of response, complaint handling, action records, press notices, leaflets and other literature, presentation and display); Monitoring and Visits (justification, protocol, reports); Contact with the community (consultation, interaction, mutual advice, surveys, analysis of enquiries and complaints, promoting the CHC in community groups, liaison with community-based professionals), and the Contribution to DHA and FHSA planning processes – obviously an important new feature of the work of CHCs, and one they must be seen to be doing well.

These were fed by ACHCEW into a more detailed project, put together and managed by Christine Hogg, with the aim of producing a comprehensive, definitive list of the standards applicable to CHCs in all their activities, and in their internal organisation. Many of the biggest names in the CHC world were involved in the reference group (advisory committee) for this project, which was clearly seen as an undertaking of great strategic importance. The intention was that the outcome of the project should be presented to the ACHCEW annual meeting in 1993. The record of the meeting states simply that Christine Hogg introduced her paper "Performance Standards for CHCs – Developing the Framework", and that after discussion and debate, it was endorsed.

If resolutions of the annual meetings of ACHCEW are any indicator of the mood of CHCs, the message coming from these years is not one of anxiety. The 1990 meeting found time to debate a motion complaining that the chief officers of CHCs were being enticed into taking jobs in health authorities with similar responsibilities, but with far higher salaries, which placed CHCs at a disadvantage in attempting to retain quality staff (this resolution may have been one of the factors leading to a number of chief officers being offered performance related pay); and another aiming to enlarge the standing committee "to make use of the undoubted talent available in CHCs at the national level" given that "the rationale for reduction in its size in 1983/84 no longer exists".

The main body of resolutions on the structure of the NHS turned around the relationship of CHCs to health authorities, trusts and fundholding GPs, and the lack of observer or consultation rights in relation to the Provider side of the reorganised NHS. Much attention was given to adverse aspects of the community care regime affecting physically or mentally disabled and psychiatric patients; to family health services complaints procedures, and to the virtual disappearance of NHS dentistry.

In 1992, a resolution calling for consultation between health authorities and CHCs over plans to merge health districts and the consequences for the local CHCs (proposed by two of the Bristol councils) was adopted, but had no effect on the final arrangements made; and in 1993 the AGM called for the NHS Ombudsman to be empowered to consider complaints against CHCs. The meeting also advised the Secretary of State, (by then Virginia Bottomley), in making the wide ranging review of NHS complaints practice she had announced, to make full use of the experience of CHCs in this field, and instructed the standing committee to produce detailed evidence by way of assistance to her. With one or two possible surprises such as the Ombudsman decision, it was very much business as usual.

The year 1994 was notable for the government's announcement that regional health authorities were to be abolished. One of the longest running institutions of the 1973 reorganisation, and for twenty-two years establishing authorities for the CHCs in England, they were to be replaced by a network of regional offices of the NHS Executive. There would be fewer regional offices than there had been RHAs, and this would bring about a restructuring of the English regions in line with current government thinking and the provider/purchaser split in health services introduced by the NHS and Community Care Act of 1990.

Under this legislation, district health authorities (a 1982 invention) had ceased to be the managers of hospital and community health services in their localities, and had become the purchasers or commissioners (and thus the customers) of health services provided by hospitals or trusts throughout the country. The internal market in the health service had been created, changing the pattern of administration in the NHS and introducing a new tension into the relationships between those who offered health care services and those who purchased them.

At the same time a new force had emerged in the land in the shape of fundholding GPs: doctors with budgets who themselves had the power to commission health care from other parts of the NHS. In this new world, with the monolithic health authority structure broken up into large fragments and a competitive ethos replacing the former unified front (which in spite of the 1973 reorganisation had remained fairly well intact since 1948), the need for fourteen administrative regions was less obvious than formerly. The creation of new medical schools in some of the newer universities had altered the concept of NHS regions as being founded on a university hospital or group of hospitals, and this too had strengthened the movement towards change, small regions based on universities such as Oxford, Cambridge or Liverpool now no longer seeming to be essential. The regional structure which had been part of the health service since its introduction was therefore scrapped, and administration became vested in eight outlying regional offices of the Department of Health.

The announcement of this change was made in 1994 in order to allow a two-year transition period, so that the necessary machinery would be in place by the time it was effected in 1996. CHCs had two years in which to prepare themselves for yet another organisational restructuring, and a new set of paymaster/superintendents. Once again, a current of uncertainty, if not anxiety, could be discerned among

CHCs; the Chair of ACHCEW advising Dr Brian Mawhinney at the 1994 AGM of the "concerns of CHCs about their future establishing arrangements once RHAs were abolished". Dr Mawhinney used the opportunity to enlarge on the government's plans to link CHCs to the regional offices of the NHS Executive, and must have answered their questions to the satisfaction of those present, since no attempt was made during the remainder of the meeting to revert to the subject.

They seemed more concerned with the potential of CHCs to provide useful information on the NHS to the public, asking for this function as an official duty; and with their response to the Wilson committee report on NHS complaints machinery, and their vision of a defined role for themselves in the new procedures it proposed. Neither of the latter materialised, and by 1996 CHCs were beginning to see some of their original reservations regarding the regional NHS offices as possibly justified.

Two other developments during this period may be regarded as significant. One of these was the Private Finance Initiative (PFI), introduced into the NHS, as into other public services, as a means of funding capital projects using private money, and 'buying back' the investment over a period of years. Since its inception this has been a highly controversial method of raising capital, attracting hostility for the use of private capital in public investment, and for the long term cost, which it is argued, far outweighs the short-term gain. These arguments notwithstanding, the PFI has been systematically used by both governments over the past twelve years, with significant applications in education and public transport as well as in health. The AGM of ACHCEW in 1996 adopted a resolution opposing its use.

The second development was the use of Citizens' Juries as a means of aiding public decision-making. Citizens' juries are created by bringing together a small group of people with the broad characteristics of the general public (educational attainment, ethnic balance etc.), to examine particular topics and policy options. Information is given to them by 'expert witnesses' under a procedure analogous to that of a court of law, and having deliberated on the evidence presented, the jury reach and announce their conclusions. Governments, intending governments, and public authorities can make use of juries in the same way as focus groups, and the two may be seen as alternatives. In 1995 and 1996 the notion of citizens' juries was being fed into the NHS by think tanks, and interest was shown by no less a body than the King's Fund.

As an enthusiastic supporter of community health councils, I was strongly suspicious of these means of information gathering, seeing them as a way of avoiding genuine public consultation, and susceptible to manipulation by methods such as the use of selective evidence to achieve the outcome desired. My concern was that they might be held up as a reason for dropping CHCs as a barometer of public opinion, and thus threatening one element of their foundation. Those active in CHCs at the time seemed to me less nervous, not being unduly perturbed by the interest shown among health bodies, and not apparently wishing to make an issue of them. Even the advice given them by ACHCEW seemed quite calm, dealing primarily with questions of procedure and the independence of the organisers. In any event, the use of citizens' juries did not turn out to be material in the demise of CHCs, and interest in them appears to have dwindled after the 1997 election.

But the quest for performance standards continued, and in 1995 the NHS Executive engaged a firm of management consultants to advise on an equitable distribution of resources to CHCs throughout England, by means of constructing a "Notional CHC" against which performance measures could be made and resource requirements calculated. The consultants chosen were Insight Management Consulting, and their report, which was published in November 1996, became known as "The Insight Report". Working through the ACHCEW files in the weeks before the association closed down, I was amazed at the volume of papers, documents and correspondence filed under that heading. It was, of course, the case that ACHCEW played quite an important part in the preparation of the report, having been represented, along with the Society of CHC Staff, on the original working group examining the implications for CHCs of the abolition of RHAs, and thus being party to the recommendation that consultants should be appointed. The files included preparatory documents, working papers and drafts for various sections of the report, as well as all the correspondence relative to it. The report itself ran to fifty-seven pages, with a further seventeen pages of appendices.

Insight started by examining the activities of CHCs and identifying four broad "core" functions, namely: (i) **consultation** with the local community and representing local needs to the health service and other interested managers; (ii) **monitoring** the quality and take up of services, and the level of satisfaction of service users and the public in general with local health and related services; (iii) **providing information and advice** to individuals and to the public generally on health and related issues, and (iv) **helping people with complaints** about the health service, or its practitioners or contractors. They went on to develop the model of the "notional CHC" by examining services in each of these four functional areas, in relation to the changing needs of patients.

Their first conclusion was "the clear view that CHCs have delivered an excellent service during their 22 years of operation". They wished to record their admiration for the way in which CHCs during that time had achieved so much for their local communities "against a backcloth of limited resources, and significant and continuing changes in the NHS". They added that:

"they have proven to be adept at understanding public health interests in their broadest sense and bringing this to the attention of those who can improve those services. In other cases... they have developed and provided services themselves where they have identified gaps in local provision. CHCs' independent position has been at the centre of their achievements so far,"

but went on to say that in their view, the changes in the NHS since 1974, particularly the most recent ones, should lead to *some* adjustment by *some* CHCs (my italics) in their activities and in their relationship with their health authority. Insight were confident that this could be effected without compromising the role of CHCs, and in support of this position, they cited CHCs which had already made changes of this kind. They commented that "the move to a strategic position has been encouraged in at least one region for some time and is considered locally to be... successful." They believed that its general adoption would necessitate some training for members and chief officers so that they could understand how to achieve maximum effectiveness in a strategic role, and that operating at this level would require continuing attention to "information gathering from direct contact with patients and the public and a range of visiting and project strategies."

What did they mean by strategic in this context? It seems clear that what they had in mind was a switch from reacting to situations created by others, to being part of the situation-creating team. From the outset, CHCs had been designed to respond both to the public and to the health authorities. During the RAWP period in the 1970s they had often found themselves reacting to situations they were powerless to alter, and while many had tried (with varying success) to get out of that position by working in collaboration with their authorities, the potential for further such problems was always latent in the background. Insight took the view that with the provider/purchaser split in the NHS, and the consequent emphasis placed by health authorities on quality of service and patient satisfaction, partnerships of this kind between them and CHCs were more likely to be workable and successful.

They therefore proposed that CHCs should seek to work with their respective authorities in the strategic role of jointly evolving services, with the CHC securing its information through its contacts in the community and using the knowledge gained this way to help shape the scale and scope of services rather than simply responding to decisions made elsewhere. They recognised that this was a departure from the traditional CHC role, and would require some reorganisation of thought processes.

As a separate issue, this adjustment would necessitate a change to the interactions between the CHC and the community. They would now be seeking specific feedback, often of a quantitative or qualitative nature, and so instead of asking open-ended questions and aggregating the answers received, they would have to deal in pointed questions and expect a reasoned, or at least a considered response.

I am not suggesting that either of these operational practices was completely new to CHCs. In fact I am faintly surprised that the consultants might have considered them novel, because I am satisfied that CHCs had had the tactical ability to spot their potential at a far earlier stage in their life. As just one example of both techniques, by about 1980 Marcia Saunders (Chief Officer of Islington CHC) and her chair Gwen Dain, were well into persuading the Islington DMT of the desirability of hand-in-hand working with the CHC, offering free feedback from the local public as an inducement. At the same time West Birmingham CHC were running a panel of 200–250 residents (perhaps the prototype for a citizens' jury) to whom they fed regular information from and about the CHC, and through whom they were able to get a regular picture of general or specific public opinion on health matters in their district as and when the need dictated. Margaret Lovell (Chapter Five) also commented on moves in this direction coming from health authority managers. It may of course have been that a number of CHCs with which Insight had dealings had not made any attempt to adopt either of these positions, and that even if the notion was familiar, putting it into effect would have been an innovation.

It is quite possible to agree with Insight's conclusions regarding the consultation and monitoring functions of CHCs. It was when they turned their attention to information giving, advice and complaints handling that they became more controversial. From their own figures, it was evident that CHCs attached much weight to these functions, since they typically incurred some 49.7% of their staff costs in performing them, compared with 22.3% on consultation and monitoring activities (Insight Report, Figure 3).

Insight on the other hand thought that CHCs were spending money needlessly on High Street premises in view of the relatively small number of people dropping in with queries or complaints. From a simple analysis of numbers and costs this position is justifiable, but it ignores the 24-hour value of the name on the fascia and the window display in reminding the public of the presence of the CHC, and conveying something of what it does. Many CHCs would also have regarded the occupation of High Street premises as more than just for attracting visitors; they would have seen it as a springboard from which other activities (such as shop-window campaigns; opinion seeking, or health promotion events) could be launched. If forced into a justification in accounting terms, they would have spread the cost over other areas of their work, rather than attributing it entirely to information and publicity.

In addition, Insight recommended that CHCs should withdraw from the business of producing printed leaflets on health matters, leaving it to health authorities and other information-giving agencies, and confining themselves to "providing advice by strengthening links with other information providers". They did concede a possible need for project-related and precisely targeted information, but concluded that their own 'notional CHC' would spend next to nothing on information giving.

In the realm of complaints, Insight set out the position as they saw it:

> "involvement in dealing with complaints has followed identification of a local need for help... Until recently there has been a real gap in such support, and CHCs have been entrepreneurial in responding to this need."

They pointed to the new complaints procedures introduced into the NHS, and reasoned that under this more equitable regime, CHCs should be "actively supporting the implementation of the new NHS complaints systems and playing a leading role in advising those who are trying to implement the new systems". In effect, they suggested that CHCs should collaborate in the application of procedures which were as yet unproven, and take up a position closer to the authorities than to the complainants.

I am aware that the redress of grievances was not a role formally given to CHCs and that the volume of work done in this area varied greatly from one CHC to another, but this was a strange reading of "the people's voice in the NHS". It assumes, first, that the procedures are intrinsically satisfactory; second, that they are fairly balanced between the NHS and complainants; third, that the authorities will use them properly, and fourth, that justice can be seen to be done at the end. Having experienced current NHS complaints procedures within my own family, I am in no doubt that these assumptions are incorrect, and that the idea of taking away the role of "patient's friend" from CHCs would have devalued both the procedures and the CHC in the public view.

What the consultants were offering CHCs was a counselling role, but shorn of the advocacy element which in my opinion is the essential concomitant. They went so far as to propose that councils should stand back from handling complaints, confining themselves to periodic comment on the quality of the procedures and the lessons that can be learned from the complaints registered. It would also be possible to scale down their complaints function to an advisory role on procedure. The result would be that CHCs would be free to apply greater effort to "other, *more strategic* areas of the local health debate".

I have placed emphasis on this last statement, since it seems to me to demonstrate a lack of comprehension on the part of Insight. Complaints are immensely important, and it can be said that all the main turning points in the history of the NHS have arisen out of failures of the system. Whether initiated by employees or by users of the service, all complaints have the potential to create shock waves, and nothing can remain under cover indefinitely. Even single or isolated complaints can turn out to have devastating repercussions and consequences of strategic dimension. The idea of community health councils was first germinated in the wake of the long-stay hospital scandals of the 1960s, and CHCs themselves lived to experience Alder Hey, Bristol Royal Infirmary and Harold Shipman. I find it astonishing that a firm of management consultants paid for by the Department of Health and working closely with CHCs should feel able to say that the complaints function is of only minor strategic significance.

This thought leads to another reflection on Insight, that throughout their report there is a sense that the 1996 snapshot is the total picture. Despite the history of regular change in NHS management and practice, and its impact on CHCs over the years between 1974 and 1996, there is no apparent dynamic, other than that of the changes immediately preceding compilation of their report. Above all, there is no *insight* into the possibility of further change to come, which to the informed observer would seem (on past performance) to be an absolute certainty.

However, Insight assembled a "notional CHC" using their own conception of the four core functions. For the sake of clarity, though at the risk of some repetition, I set out what this entailed:

Consultation: the notional CHC will have a sufficiently well developed local network to provide it with accurate information about the nature, purpose and potential impact of local initiatives. It therefore draws on the results of other people's work, enabling effective consultative processes to develop naturally. Its effectiveness lies in representing its public by working with, and influencing the health authority during the development of its plans, based on a solid understanding of local health interests.

Monitoring: it is founded on a shift of emphasis in monitoring objectives and activities in response to changes in the business environment and local needs. Its influence is enhanced by targeting its activities on identifying and investigating the community's needs and interests in specific areas rather than across the board working and its contribution to health authority planning is made from a position of knowledge and aimed at filling gaps in health care provision.

Information and Advice: the CHC will establish whether existing information services are meeting local need, and recommend any changes in provision that it considers appropriate. It will provide advice by strengthening its links with other sources of information, but will retain the capability of advising the public on how to complain about NHS services.

Complaints: it will best serve its local community by actively supporting the implementation of the (new) NHS complaints systems and advising those who are trying to put them into effect. In doing so, it will also work with the public and the health service providers locally to identify and define a new role and *modus operandi*.

This CHC will engage in performance management through its annual workplans and reports; by performance review (it will operate an augmented version of the biennial Peer Group Review process) and by the application of formal project management techniques to all its tasks. It will be statutorily accountable to the Secretary of State for Health through the NHS Executive, and locally to the community through the publication of its annual workplans and reports, and through its meetings, which are open to the public and press, and offer adequate opportunity for comment or criticism of its work.

I had expected the circle to have been completed by an empirical analysis of the costs of this CHC derived from those of councils which had already moved in the direction described, with a pointer towards the financial and other resource needs for CHCs in general that adoption of the "notional CHC" model would imply. Unfortunately, as the consultants explained at an early stage in their report:

> "Although we found a consensus on what are the broad CHC functions, we also found significant differences in local practice in carrying out these functions, arising at least partly from significant differences in local need. The absence of standard practices, coupled with an absence of common definitions (for example, of

what constitutes a complaint), led us to conclude that at present, 'notional CHC' activities could not be costed."

They made this a double blow by adding that they could find "no single, logical basis in current... practices... to begin the search for a more equitable and objective formula" they could use as a base for future funding recommendations.

They were thus reduced after quite a lengthy discussion to recommending that for each region a sum broadly proportional to the regional hospital and community health services budget should be allocated for CHCs. Across the country, this would not make a very great aggregate change to the amount of money spent on them, but certain regional allocations would be substantially enlarged, while others would see major reductions. These new levels of regional funding should be apportioned among CHCs according to the system of funding currently being used, but they would have to be phased over several years to permit the heavier losing regions and their CHCs to adjust to the new funding levels applicable.

The Insight report must have been a disappointment to CHCs in a number of respects, notably in its failure to find a resourcing formula, but equally in the number of other questions it left unanswered and the imprecision of some of its key recommendations, in particular the operational picture of the "notional CHC" including its staffing and accommodation. It was probably a greater disappointment still to the NHS Executive, which had paid for it and had certainly hoped to get palpable answers and value for money out of it. CHCs were perhaps to some degree inured to uncertainty, having been covering much of the same ground themselves for the previous seven years or more, but even so expectations had been raised, and at the end, the whole experience is bound to have left them feeling rather flat.

Chapter Seven

The Last Lap

"Change is needed. There are a number of options for the future. Whatever route is chosen… must build on the experience of twenty years of CHCs"

(Christine Hogg, "Back from the Margins", IHSM, 1996)

After the report, the debate on Insight. Once the report had been published and all concerned had made their comments on it, the question that then arose was whether it should be implemented in full or in part, or whether it should be acted upon at all. My contacts in community health councils in general did not have much to say to me about it. Geoff Ellam, who at the time was chief officer of Camden CHC in London was the only person who gave me a spontaneous opinion: "when regions began to appoint their CHC 'leads' from the ranks of chief officers, things began to look up – especially in the training of CHC staff and members – but this was too little and too late. The Insight team had by then done quite a good job, I thought, but it had been roundly attacked by almost the whole CHC world. Why couldn't we have had a constructive debate around their recommendations?"

Toby Harris explained to me that from his point of view, the engagement of Insight was a sign of real interest in CHCs on the part of ministers. They were prepared to put some resources into getting a sense of how the councils operate and to use the knowledge gained in an attempt to produce an outcome that was beneficial to CHCs rather than negative. Against this background, he was keen to encourage as constructive as possible a response from CHCs, and to put certain positive outcomes into the mind of the consultants. Among the latter, he instanced more training for staff and members; the principle of peer review, and CHC-led standard setting. "We didn't get all that agenda, but some of it certainly did follow on from the Insight report" was his conclusion.

By March 1997, ACHCEW had produced its own response to Insight, in the shape of a paper comprising twenty-three recommendations made by the association as well as a further two recommendations, and amendments to eleven of the original ACHCEW recommendations added by member CHCs. While certain elements of these thirty-six propositions relate directly to the role and relationships of the "notional CHC", the document as a whole reads more like a wish-list of the rights and functions desired by CHCs in relation to providers and purchasers in the NHS (including GPs), and the resources and control mechanisms which in their view would be needed to match the new responsibilities. As such, it retains the tenor of many ACHCEW annual meeting resolutions over the preceding years, and serves as a *de facto* rejection of Insight, diffusing the argument and shifting official attention away from the recommendations the consultants had made.

It is probable that Insight had laid themselves open to this by not coming up with clear even if controversial results. A recommendation in favour of the notional CHC, or some variation on it, together with a costing and firm pointers on funding and quality assurance for CHCs would certainly have concentrated attention on the consultants' findings, and may even have attracted support among some CHCs. Had a sprinkling of secondary recommendations on working relationships with health authorities, trusts and GPs also been included, Insight's independent voice might, particularly if in any way supportive, have opened up some interesting new perspectives for CHCs, and Geoff Ellam might have had his hoped-for debate.

The lack of any particular outcome from the Insight report is perhaps immaterial, since as events have demonstrated, the CHCs in England were fated not to survive. But perhaps there is an outside chance that had there been any substantive decisions recommended by the consultants, and had some agreed proposals emerged from the subsequent debate, Labour could have been persuaded to see them as one feature of the NHS that was modernising itself, and could without loss of face have been woven into the government's forward thinking with regard to public participation in health. As Geoff Ellam said, Frank Dobson did tell ACHCEW that the writing was on the wall, "and was kind enough to read it out to us – but no one was listening."

At the end of 1996, the Association of CHCs had produced "The Patients' Agenda", a commentary on the NHS Patients' Charter, setting out a series of suggested entitlements which, in the publishers' estimation, should have been accorded to the public as rights in the NHS, but had not been part of the charter published by the government. Under seven headings, including Access to Care & Treatment; Choice & Information; Advocacy, Support & Appropriate Care; and Redress, they listed twenty-six 'agenda items' for patients, covering "areas where patients find their present rights are poor or non-existent and where their reasonable expectations are not met".

The Patients' Agenda at once provided a manifesto for extending the range of public entitlements in the NHS, and a programme of campaigning issues for users of the health service, which could be pursued singly or in groups until as many as possible were accepted by NHS management and the DoH. It drew on a wide variety of authoritative sources, including the work of medical researchers and voluntary or public representative bodies (including CHCs), and made no recommendations, allowing the patients' rights to speak for themselves. In the hands of the medical profession (the GMC, the BMA or one of the Royal Colleges) or the opposition parties in parliament, the content and timing of this paper would have made it big enough news for the media to run it prominently for several days, reviving it from time to time when some controversial copy on the NHS was needed to enliven an otherwise news-free day. For all the quality of the work and the evident public interest value of the subject matter, CHCs sadly did not have the same media sex appeal, and although well received, the Patients' Agenda did not keep the front pages filled in the way it might have done, had it originated from a different source. Any impact it made was confined to secondary opinion formers such as magazine journalists or research workers in neighbouring fields.

Back at the drawing board, CHCs in the South Western region were working on a performance management system and in February 1997, they published a series of recommendations under the headings of Strategy Planning and Monitoring, Quality Monitoring and Evaluation, Relationships and Communications, and Organisational Arrangements which were influential in ensuing discussions between ACHCEW and the Department of Health. This is evidenced by a letter to Toby Harris from the NHS Executive dated 7 November 1997, the tone of which makes clear the Executive's anxiety to get an agreed performance measurement system into place. The central portion reads:

"Various strands of work on performance management and review processes are currently being examined in a number of regions. In particular a performance evaluation framework has been developed by CHCs in the South and West Region. The framework does appear to have a number of merits: it has been developed by CHCs themselves, it builds on previous work on CHC performance standards, it offers flexibility of application depending on a CHC's stage of development on performance management and it is

183

able to incorporate complementary review processes such as the peer review process being piloted in South Thames. Regional CHCs leads are taking the views of their CHCs on it and interest has been expressed in adopting it or a variation of it in a number of regions.

"Given the useful basis which the South and West framework offers, the interest in it and the risk of reinventing the wheel in starting from scratch we would not propose to initiate any specific new development work in this area."

Or in plain language, "the system created by the South Western CHCs is good enough for us, and we don't want to waste time looking for something more sophisticated." This blunt statement notwithstanding, no decisive progress had been made by August 1998, when Toby Harris was being asked to give comments on "the revised version of the performance evaluation framework" by Monday 5 October. But by that time Toby had become Lord Harris of Haringey, and no longer needed to worry about such matters.

Shortly after the change of government, ACHCEW published a prospectus of the services it offered member CHCs. These included four different sets of publications, two of them (*Community Health Council News* and *CHC Listings*) appearing ten times per year, and between them offering something akin to the *CHC News* of my day. The remaining two were information papers: on the one hand, short briefing papers entitled "Health Perspectives" produced by ACHCEW staff and covering topics of interest or concern, such as access to NHS dentistry or the impact of the new government on the health service; and on the other, a series of research papers going into greater depth on matters of importance to CHCs. These might be researched and written internally, or commissioned from authors knowledgeable or highly reputed in the area of health policy, management, research or interest they covered.

In addition, ACHCEW provided an information service (again analogous to the original information service closed down in 1984); a training arm for CHCs, and a legal advice service, providing information and guidance for them in relation to the performance of their functions. Among its standard services, ACHCEW also provided the national forum for its members, organised conferences and seminars, and promoted the interests of CHCs in making their point of view known to government, opinion formers and the national media, and producing advertising and publicity material.

ACHCEW in 1997 had far greater resources than twenty years earlier, a more extensive archive, a longer history and a proportionally larger membership. It was able to produce more published work, to a level of academic and political quality to which at the outset we could only aspire. Acknowledging all this, it is reassuring to look at this prospectus and to find that its elements differ in practically no respect (other than the training facility for CHCs, which in the 1970s we could not even have envisaged) from the services negotiated for members in the earliest days. Even the legal service was one which, as I mentioned in an earlier chapter, had been put into place in a limited way by 1980 under the care of John Finch of Leicester University, and was still running when I left for Shetland, but fell victim to the financial crisis of 1984.

ACHCEW achieved a notable consensus at its 1998 AGM in Birmingham, and took a major step towards a public accountability standard with the debate and agreement of a series of core policy priorities for CHCs. In the space of a one-hour pre-lunch session, eight priorities were adopted, in two cases entailing acceptance of several sub-priorities. The total package set a wide range of obligations for CHCs in their relationship with their communities, which in the light of previous discussion is worth setting out here as confirmation of the point that had been reached in the eighteen months since the Insight report:

Core Policy Priorities for Community Health Councils (1998)

CPP 1: To monitor the quality and take-up and the level of satisfaction of service users and the public with local health and health-related services, and report as appropriate to the relevant health authority, to local primary care groups and to service providers.

CPP 1.1: to establish relationships with local primary care groups and to offer to report to them on a regular basis in relation to CHC monitoring of local services.

CPP 1.2: to consider and inform the work being done by the local health authority in monitoring the quality of local services.

CPP 1.3: to maintain a dialogue with local service providers in relation to the work done by the CHC and by the service provider in monitoring the quality of services provided.

CPP 2: To respond, where appropriate, to consultation and planning documents on health and health-related matters, in particular in respect of proposals for substantial development or variations in service.

CPP 2.1: to seek to achieve an input into the preparation of the Health Improvement Programme for the area and to respond to the formal consultation on the draft.

CPP 2.2: to develop a dialogue with local primary care groups on their commissioning plans and intentions and to encourage them to consult on these more generally.

CPP 2.3: to encourage local service providers to consult the CHC and service users on their plans for the services they provide.

CPP 2.4: to seek involvement by the CHC in the preparation of any proposals for capital developments in the area.

CPP 3: To recommend improvements in services, to comment on the assessments made by the relevant authorities of local needs, and to seek to influence the range, type and quality of services commissioned and provided for the local population.

CPP 4: To ensure, by consulting and reporting widely and maintaining good community links, that the public is notified of issues of local concern and is advised of the work of the CHC and its actions on the public's behalf.

CPP 5: To promote better access to health and health-related services for black and minority ethnic groups, disabled people, and other groups and individuals who may be disadvantaged in the delivery of services, and to seek to ensure that services are provided in a manner appropriate to their needs.

CPP 6: To support the promotion of good health in the locality and to encourage local debate on the public health agenda that should be followed by local agencies and organisations.

CPP 7: By assisting people who have complaints about the health service or against NHS practitioners or contractors, to pursue the issues raised by complaints and to monitor the operation of the complaints system locally.

CPP 8: To demonstrate that the CHC is delivering an effective service that is value for money to the local community.

There, in a nutshell, are the ambitions (in service terms) of CHCs in mid-1998. It follows that if these functional policy priorities were accepted, it would be necessary to back them with the proper level of resources, in staff and financial terms, to allow their successful implementation. The proposal therefore was to extend the functions of CHCs, with a matching increase in their financial allocations.

The picture it paints has features in common with the 'notional CHC' in terms of its closer links with the authorities in consultation and joint working, and in the absence to any reference to information and advice giving. On the other hand, it does not exclude this function, and there is no mention of links with information-giving agencies. It gives considerable weight to the monitoring process, and rather more so than the notional CHC; this clearly being a matter of importance, if not of high levels of expenditure, among CHCs. Finally, it emphatically includes attention to patients' complaints and the redress of grievances, both as a service to the community and as a basis for monitoring the effectiveness of the complaints machinery and impressing the service implications on the authorities. While the NHS Executive might not wish to concede this manifesto to the letter, it could be in little doubt of what CHCs wanted – and were prepared to be judged on – and that they were now, perhaps for the first time in twenty-five years, all pulling in the same direction.

This unaccustomed unanimity may have been inspired by a paper prepared for the Institute of Health Services Management and ACHCEW by Christine Hogg, and entitled "Back from the Margins". This, in my view, is one of three outstanding works on CHCs produced during the period 1996–1999. Its starting point was that community health councils "are under-developed, under-valued, and without doubt under-resourced for the role they are expected to play". It also claimed that some had been marginalized and were not taken seriously. From there it moved on to trace the history of CHCs from their foundation in 1974, setting out in a simple table their rights and duties in relation to health authorities.

It then looked at the activities in which CHCs were engaged, and classified them in terms of the mediating position they adopted between the public they served and the authorities to which they represented the public interest. Next, the paper examined the accountability of CHCs and their staff; the limitations under which they worked and the resources available to them, concluding that "CHCs have had a significant impact in changing attitudes in the NHS towards patients", and that given their cost to the nation, "the contribution of CHCs in involving local people and opening up the NHS to public scrutiny represents good value for money".

From this introduction, "Back from the Margins" went on to chart the situation as it was at the time of writing. First, it pointed to ways in which the rights of CHCs had been eroded by changes in NHS operational structures; where influence was shifting from health authorities alone in the direction of NHS trusts and general practitioners, with whom they had no representational or consultative rights. Second, it traced the ways in which the changed role of health authorities from managers to purchasers of health services had led to their intrusion into territory previously occupied by CHCs only. In some cases this had resulted in duplication, and in others to productive joint initiatives – in health needs assessments, public consultation, user surveys and advice or information services for example. Third, it looked into CHCs' relationships with NHS Trusts, and the desirability of their continuation to both sides, pointing up cases where collaboration between trusts and CHCs had been mutually beneficial. Fourth, it studied CHC involvement with complaints in the light of the Patients' Charter, and the pressure caused by the resultant increase in public expectations and the lack of any new resources for CHCs to meet this need. This section was illustrated by examples from Salford, Durham and Bradford, where CHCs had worked with local health services to prevent complaints from arising. Fifth, it turned to primary and community care services, and the difficulties for CHCs in establishing a systematic involvement in these aspects of treatment and care. Illustrations in this section showed how nonetheless it had been possible in some locations for CHCs, general practitioners and Social Services to make use of each others' skills to meet jointly perceived needs.

The conclusion from drawing these strands together was that all the changes in the NHS since 1990 had increased the remit of CHCs and the pressures on them. Every factor influencing their performance was at once a strength and a weakness (their independence, for example, could be reinterpreted as isolation) and something had to be done "to help them become more effective and bring them out from the margins and into the centre of the health system".

The final part of "Back from the Margins" took a leap into the future. It stressed the need for change, but insisted that "this must build on the experiences gained from twenty years of CHCs". It suggested the establishment of an independent agency to take over the role of establishing authority for CHCs, with standard setting and audit included in its remit. On the other hand, it emphasised the need for CHCs to get into their communities and truly to reflect their aspirations and priorities. It urged stronger and more prescriptive rights for CHCs, matched by a two-way accountability: to the community and to the standard-setting parent body. Resources allocated to CHCs should match the national expectation of what a public watchdog should do.

A range of possibilities, including the abolition or restyling of CHCs, was examined, and the most promising alternative role was identified in community development, as an enabler and facilitator for a more vocal and more demanding local constituency. The conclusion from this section was that the role of CHCs "should be enhanced to enable them to empower users and local communities, and to assist people, both as groups and individuals, to participate in health and social care".

Having spelled out the main changes this would necessitate in the remit, rights and responsibilities of CHCs, and the concomitant enhancements in their accountability and the capability of their members and staff it would demand, the paper's final word on the subject was "A national strategy that does not use enhanced CHCs to develop a local framework for empowerment and participation is likely to fail".

"Back from the Margins" was one of the most powerful papers written during this period in the life of CHCs, and was widely read and discussed among their members and employees. It was published early enough to influence thinking at the time of the Insight study and report, and to have seeped into the "Patients' Agenda" and the later Core Policy Priorities. And yet in a strange way it reads as if it came after them; as if it had been written when all these arguments had been brought to a conclusion, and what was then needed was to mould that conclusion into a blueprint for the second term of office of the government, with the changes it was likely to bring.

The prescient, almost prophetic tone of the concluding section is quite striking, and since the fate awaiting CHCs was read in the cards by Christine Hogg as early as January 1996, it is perhaps surprising that neither ACHCEW (its joint publisher) nor its membership appear to have made it one of their longer term considerations as the seemingly sterile and circular argument with the NHS Executive on performance standards and accountability ground on. Of course, the Trojans didn't listen to Cassandra either.

ACHCEW itself produced a key paper towards the end of 1997, in the shape of "CHCs Making a Difference". This was not just a defiant trumpet blast: it was a genuine compilation of the constructive and painstaking work of CHCs in every part of England and Wales, giving credit where it was due, and noting successes, both great and small. As a morale booster, it had something to offer for every CHC in the country, with more than half of them mentioned by name; as propaganda, it had a more convincing story to tell than many hundreds of pages of PR copy. It was not trying to sell CHCs to the world; it was simply telling the truth.

CHCs began to make a difference in about September 1974, as soon as their chief officers were appointed and they began to examine their own health districts. Stories of achievements, major and minor, are documented in annual reports from 1975 onwards. Whatever one's conception of CHCs, it is impossible not to acknowledge that they have improved the experience people have had over the years from the NHS in many ways, and practically never made it any worse. "CHCs Making a Difference" should therefore come as no surprise. Its importance lies in putting together a large number of beneficial actions by CHCs, and reminding the reader that this is about their everyday work and what results from it.

A glance through the contents page shows the range of subject matter covered. Examples of positive activity are to be found in Primary Care (general practice; practice developments; GP's out of hours services; dentists and pharmacists), Hospital Care (quality assurance; clinical care; new services; hospital food; accessibility; privacy and dignity; outpatients; discharge; ambulance services and transport) and Services for Client Groups (maternity; children; older people; mental health; disability; terminal care), as well as the work of CHCs in monitoring quality and influencing improvements, and in giving advice and help to complainants or people in need. The second part of the paper explains the work of community health councils and how their time is used, and discusses questions of efficiency, effectiveness, quality assurance, and how they can be improved. The influence of Christine Hogg's work is evident, and is acknowledged in the text as well as in the references.

These two works are complementary, and together form a major segment of CHC literature. It is not the case that neither could have been written without the other, but having been written during the same period they view their subject from two distinct standpoints in one single timescale, and thus have the impact of two spotlights in sharpening its illumination. Had this bright light been used to advantage, CHCs might have been able to put themselves in an unassailable position over the following two and a half years. As just one example, use could have been made of a comment in "CHCs Making a Difference" to the effect that the two main criticisms of CHCs made by health authorities appear to be largely contradictory, and quoting:

> "CHCs are unprofessional, because unpaid, untrained, do not know what they are doing, and are not sufficiently well informed"... and "CHCs are not like the general public, they are not representative of the public, seen as being another structured organisation (i.e. *too well informed*, etc.)."

The third of my triptych of key publications from about this time is one to which I have referred earlier. It is entitled *At The Crossroads*, and was written by Chris Dabbs, chief officer of Salford CHC as a dissertation for a degree and published in January 1999. The size of this book is such, and the research element so intensive, that he must have been working on it at least for the whole of 1998. His bibliography is comprehensive (with 585 references), and includes both

"Back from the Margins" and "CHCs Making a Difference" as sources. Chris Dabbs' starting point is that to face the future with confidence, CHCs have to change: "the one option that should not be entertained is the *status quo*. To leave CHCs largely the same... will leave them increasingly weakened and marginalized. Arguments for minor change – or none at all – will leave the citizens of England and Wales less well represented and protected than could and should be the case... CHCs cannot afford to stand still. The time has come for a 'biological' renewal. From a chrysalis may emerge a stronger and more beautiful creature, ready to take on the world."

In his own words, Chris Dabbs' study aimed to review the effectiveness of CHCs and to develop options for the future. While CHCs had many achievements and strengths, they were neither as efficient or effective as they might be. Collectively, they lacked focus and were highly variable. They were largely dependent on their chief officers. There was a need for radical thinking and change. Two possible main focuses for activity presented themselves as alternative ways forward, in the shape of service provision and health improvement. Equally, there were two possible basic functions for CHCs: independent monitoring and scrutiny, or the direct involvement and participation of lay people.

After careful analysis of every operational aspect of the life of CHCs and the interactions (positive and negative) implicit in them, Chris proposed four working models which he termed "health and social services councils", "citizens' involvement councils", "public health councils" and "health improvement councils". He set out the notional functions of each, and discussed at some length the organisational structure into which they might fit, and the issues surrounding their accountability, staffing and membership.

This is an impressive and thoughtful piece of work, and while I don't find any of the four models particularly appealing – I am closest to the Citizens' Involvement pattern, but would prefer a more active role in complaints and advocacy – there is no question that Chris Dabbs assembled a mass of information about CHCs, and how they and others saw them, much of which was possibly unknown to many before he brought it together in one volume. Dealing with each sub-topic as he did by SWOT analysis (assessing the capability of CHCs to deal with it and the pitfalls along the way), Chris presented a cautionary perspective for those who might have wished to run ahead, but at the same time forewarned them of the risks and equipped them better for the journey they would have to take. I took *At The Crossroads* round the world with me, when visiting family in Australia and New Zealand in 2004, and never regretted doing so. I am only sorry that it was not published in a more permanent form, as it deserves to be available on library shelves.

These three documents are a meaningful part of the history of CHCs, since they amount to a recognition that times were changing, and that what was acceptable at the outset and in the pioneering phase would not pass muster twenty-five years later. Although it was government thinking in 1973 that was at fault, and CHCs were only the creation of the powers that be, unless they took action to restyle themselves in order to seem acceptable to the government of the day, it would be they which would be held responsible for their shortcomings and would suffer the consequences.

Peter Walsh, who was Director of ACHCEW in 2002, says that in the final three years, CHCs had become so convinced of this that "not only was there no resistance to the idea of radical changes to the way CHCs work(ed)... but a positive thirst for it". So, the ideas put forward by Christine Hogg, Ben Griffith (who wrote "CHCs Making a Difference" for ACHCEW) and Chris Dabbs had taken much wider root, and were not just part of the collective wisdom, but a positive objective for early action. This was a historic change.

As long ago as 1976 in his booklet "CHCs in Action" Jack Hallas had written that: "NHS managers are making a career. They come and go, and wish to stamp their own personality on the district in which they are working at the time, as an investment in their own future. It is unrealistic to expect of them a comparable level of commitment to the district and its communities to [that of] members of the CHC". Christine Hogg frequently made similar observations, and I have quoted Toby Harris on the "macho" manager elsewhere.

Margaret Lovell, summarising developments in the NHS during the 1990s for me, remarked that the introduction of fixed-term contracts and targets for NHS managers meant that "at local level there was much more of a 'change, and change it quickly, and then move on' culture developing, which further disadvantaged CHCs (which might be) working over longer-term periods with (a broader) vision of what health services should look like" in their own locality. Most CHCs, in her view, wanted reform to enable them to raise their own performance in the interests of their local population, and the absence of progress in this area was compounded by the "chop and change" (or perhaps "cut and paste") attitude they now had to endure in the behaviour of local management. It is perhaps as well that the regional health authorities had by this time ceased to exist, since if, like the South Western region in 1979, they had wanted to press CHCs to reflect the views of managers to the public, they might have been quite embarrassed by the message that emerged.

Frank Dobson addressed the twentieth ACHCEW annual meeting in Bournemouth, shortly after the May 1997 election, and made a return visit the following year, this time in Birmingham. (Baroness) Helene Hayman was the ministerial speaker at the 1999 AGM in Eastbourne, but there was no government representative at the Harrogate meeting in 2000. This could be interpreted as ominous, given that the

AGM took place in the first week of July, and the abolition of the CHCs in England was announced in the final week of the same month. Donna Covey had taken over from Toby Harris as Director at the beginning of 1999, and Alan Hartley was elected chair in 2000. Almost as soon as she took up her duties, Donna made two determined steps in the direction of securing a future for CHCs: setting up the ACHCEW Commission on Representing the Public Interest in the Health Service under the chairmanship of Will Hutton, then Editor-in-Chief of *The Observer*, and establishing an All Party Parliamentary Group on CHCs. Both the Commission and the All Party Group were launched in February 1999. The terms of reference laid down for the Commission were to identify the ways in which the public interest can best be served by the achievement of a full and effective system of public accountability.

"New Life For Health", the report of the Commission, published early in 2000, foresaw a key role in the future for CHCs and their association. While, given its provenance, this might have been expected, the proposals were logically argued and defensible. The All Party Group was in its own way long overdue. Tony Smythe had been the first to talk of exchanging views and information systematically with MPs, and Toby Harris had put forward a similar proposal after the Insight report. But it was the initiative of Donna Covey that first brought it into existence and gave it a remit to cover the interests of Scottish Local Health Councils and Northern Irish Health and Social Service District Committees as well as the CHCs in England and Wales. Unfortunately, this Westminster voice was not as powerful as its proponents hoped, and its lifetime was depressingly brief.

During the first year of Donna's term as director of ACHCEW, CHCs, as their reports show, went about their business as normal, and in every case that I have seen, reported good working relationships between themselves and the local health services: In the case of Portsmouth and SE

Hampshire, an "active input and influence". The same CHC reported on the number of initiatives and innovative practices that had been generated and implemented locally and by sister CHCs in the region. This quite clearly suggests that CHCs were performing well within the current parameters, and there is no doubt from any quarter that their association was also under able management. That they were moving forward, and eager to embrace new practices and shift the emphasis of their work into new directions at the time they were stopped in their tracks, makes their abrupt assassination even more bewildering.

Chapter Eight

A Personal Appreciation

"The amount of work... done by CHCs is impressive; doubly so when the small size of their revenue... (is) considered. Results produced by CHCs are usually of a high standard and are always compelling enough to warrant serious consideration."

(Tom Richardson, "The Public Voice in the Health Services", Anglia and Oxford RHA, 1995)

Advising his authority on the performance of CHCs in the region, Tom Richardson informed his management that the regional CHCs:

- possessed a wealth of data from the public about the quality of local services which they had amassed over the previous twenty years, and which they were prepared to make freely available to Providers and Purchasers alike;
- were all prepared to become further involved in systematically drawing the public into the management processes of the NHS, but that they needed the resources to do so, and had to be confident that the views of the public would be acted upon by the purchasers;
- had the added virtue of being cost-effective. CHC members were committed to the NHS and spent a significant amount of their time working voluntarily in its support;

- accomplished a very considerable amount on behalf of patients and the public, but did not publicise their achievements. Few people within the NHS, and fewer still within the community generally, were aware of the extent of CHC work.
- had accumulated over twenty years a knowledge and experience of how the NHS actually works, which was largely unrecognised, and greatly underused.

What he said has a lot of truth in it, and it is to be hoped that the A&ORHA was wise enough to take him up on his offer.

Paul Reynolds, who was chief officer of Bury CHC in Greater Manchester throughout its lifetime and a leading figure in the Society of CHC Secretaries from an early stage, made known his very strong views in a letter he sent me in June 2003 in these terms:

"At the start, CHCs were in a very isolated position... NHS bodies were suspicious and in many cases resentful... while the government were floundering with the intellectual concept of public involvement... CHCs were able to attract a very high calibre of chief officer, many of whom went on to great things...

"In the early days, CHCs were left very much to their own devices... This was probably a good thing. We found our own feet and had (out of necessity) to push back the boundaries on our own...

"CHCs did that very well and became very effective in taking up issues, both local and national – to the extent that by the middle of the 1980s individuals, groups, and even NHS bodies looked to us to challenge many of the more unpopular policies of the day...

"One of our perceived weaknesses was a lack of democratic accountability – always a problem [with] appointed bodies... Democracy never bothered the government when it came to health authorities, FPCs and trusts... It is very difficult to interest people from deprived communities in [membership of] public bodies... Finding a solution to this is [equally] difficult.

"The government claimed that one of its reasons [for abolition] was the number of under-performing CHCs. It is surely not a surprise that some CHCs under performed, but we were never told how many, or how [the quality of performance] had been measured... It was probably very few, and there was ...some underlying reason. My theory is that we performed too well and had become a very effective watchdog family...

"What [nobody] seemed able to grasp was how effectively CHCs adapted and developed to meet their own local circumstances... With so few resources it was... absolutely brilliant... Eventually, so good did CHCs become at meeting... national and local challenges, drawing the public's attention to issues and standards of service that NHS management and the government would rather [had] remained opaque, that we were perceived as a threat, and of course had to go...

"I believe we have seen the golden age of public participation... delivered in a variety of ways by CHCs... What is certain is that CHCs delivered one of the one of the best values [for money] in the British public service... Bury CHC delivered a Rolls Royce to the people of Bury... [at a cost] which cannot be bettered... this is just one example among 198."

Paul speaks from absolute conviction, displaying both the passion of the committed chief officer and the pride, the shock and the widely-felt hurt I referred to in the opening chapter. His is a powerful voice, and if justice is to be done to his cause, it deserves to be heard.

A great deal has been heard on the other side of the argument, and at this point I intend to add my own appreciation to that of the friends and colleagues with whom I worked in the early days.

My first conclusion has to be that CHCs were greatly underrated. As Tom Richardson made clear, the aggregate knowledge of the NHS among the CHCs in England and their members and staff (and this applied equally to their equivalents in Wales, Scotland and Northern Ireland), and the level of commitment to the NHS as a political ideal and as a system of health care provision was no less than gigantic. That the government could jettison an asset of such massive practical and PR value at a stroke is unaccountable.

Although the quality of individual CHC members and employees was known on a personal level to a large number of NHS managers, clinicians and board members, the concept of the CHC as a competent, thoughtful and sometimes imaginative contributor to the debate on health service development as it eddied and shifted over the years, never somehow took hold. It suited many in government, in top-level management and in the front line of operational health services to be able to dismiss the CHC as amateur, or troublesome, and consequently the argument was kept at the level of 'variability' or 'interference' rather than credit being given where it was due.

There is always a thread of truth in any successful argument, however spurious. It could not be sustained otherwise. Politicians and managers at any level have an innate distrust of any group or organisation which criticises them but does not put forward an alternative strategy. In matters of government, it is said that "the duty of the opposition is to oppose", yet governments at every level have little patience with opponents who simply oppose, demanding of their opposition that they also present an alternative strategic vision. Health authorities are in a similar position, and the small number of CHCs which (mainly at the start) chose simply to oppose their proposals were not just barking up the wrong tree, but were damaging the standing of CHCs collectively, and helping to give some long-term plausibility to an argument which in truth contained very little substance.

Moving this question forward one stage, it is difficult to understand how amateurish or petty minded organisations could have produced the number of people of distinction in politics and management that have come from the ranks of CHCs. Former members or chief officers of CHCs have been ministers in all governments since 1992: the names of John Bowis, Philip Hunt and Hazel Blears have been mentioned in this book and leap at once to mind. Keith Bradley, who was an MP until 2005 also held ministerial responsibilities. Among a large number of MPs with CHC experience, John Austin has been Chair of ACHCEW. In the early 1980s, Frank Haynes left the Standing Committee to become MP for Ashfield (Nottinghamshire) and Mike McGowan to become MEP for Leeds. Toby Harris, like Philip Hunt, sits in the House of Lords. Professor Rod Griffiths has been government medical director for the West Midlands and President of the Faculty of Public Health, while ex-ACHCEW directors Donna Covey and Peter Walsh both continue to lead national voluntary organisations.

Many CHC members moved into NHS management following the 1982 reorganisation. Patricia Moberly who initially was chair of St Thomas's CHC, has for many years chaired the corresponding authority and its successor NHS Trust, and Mavis Garner who in 1982 chaired West Essex CHC, has held various chairmanships in the NHS, being chair of Royston, Buntingford and Bishops Stortford Primary Care Trust at the time of writing. These are only two, and no doubt there are many other similar examples across the country.

Perhaps the most spectacular success story is that of Marcia Saunders, who started in CHCs as assistant to chief officer Julian Knox in Islington, and has risen through chairing district health authorities in North London to be the present chair of the North Central London Strategic Health Authority and enjoys an impressive reputation as an astute health service manager. She puts her success down to having spent several years in related fields before coming back into NHS management, as well as to having "a level of historical knowledge going back some thirty years that is really quite rich, and unusual among NHS managers".

This is only the tip of the iceberg. Many former members and employees of CHCs already had professions as doctors, nurses, lawyers, engineers, scientists, clergy and academics, and have continued to pursue the vocation of their choice successfully, if without public acclaim. It is neither just nor reasonable to suggest that CHCs were somehow the inferior partner in the local NHS structure. The people they attracted were gifted and inventive. What they lacked was the resources to reinforce their reasoning and the clear authority to insist that their opinion was given its due weight.

However, they were inclined to be somewhat unruly. CHCs were always jealous of their own independence, and while ready to collaborate with neighbouring CHCs whenever issues of mutual interest arose, and aware of the need for contact with others (especially, for obvious reasons, at the regional level), their minds in general were focussed on their own district in a proprietorial way. They evolved their own working practices for their district, and insisted on their own local autonomy.

CHCs attracted people of ability, but they also attracted the sort of people whose ego matched their capabilities, and who thus had a high personal regard for themselves and the work they turned out. On its own, this is not a negative quality. It gives people enthusiasm for their work, provokes enjoyment and a sense of perfectionism that stimulates them to work well. But equally it makes them sensitive to criticism, and reluctant to take the advice of others, especially outsiders. This is one of the reasons why CHCs took so long to establish a national body; why an association was chosen in preference to a national council, and why it was not given a very warm welcome when it came into being. Even when it had proved itself to be an ally, there were numerous CHCs which preferred to keep it at arm's length, and kept their own membership conditional, that is, on their own agenda for regular debate.

It was at first a surprise to me when CHCs which had been members of ACHCEW since its inception invited me to address their AGM on the benefits of belonging to the association, and I found myself fielding questions as slippery as I got from those who had little interest in joining. After a time I came to realise that the business of retaining their confidence was a permanent effort, and success was never guaranteed. This was a constant feature of my time at ACHCEW, and because of the financial crisis of 1984, well after my departure.

It had two serious consequences. One of these was that as an association, ACHCEW could not take on the role of establishing body for CHCs, so that the opportunity which arose in 1996 to achieve autonomy following the abolition of RHAs could not be taken; the other was that ACHCEW had no enforcement capacity, and could not impose its will on CHCs, for example, with regard to targets for performance. This was a weakness in the later years, when the absence of an independent establishing and enforcement authority made it easier for ministers to consider shutting down the whole network.

Christine Hogg told me that by the early 1990s when she was addressing CHCs on setting performance evaluation standards, what struck her was how much the world had changed since she had been personally involved. When she reported to the AGM, she had expected robust criticism and some dissent from those who wished to go their own way without outside interference. In the event she was criticised for not being prescriptive, and speakers in the debate were calling for the standards to be mandatory.

Elsewhere, Christine had been critical of ACHCEW for not seizing the initiative and taking a positive lead when its members were calling for it. This change in attitude among CHCs may have been easier for an outsider to identify than for ACHCEW itself. But it is to say the least a pity that it was not spotted and a wider confirmation sought for what it implied. A great deal of time and effort might have been spared, and putting the most optimistic slant on it, so might CHCs. My intuition tells me that if Rod Griffiths had been around at the time, he would have detected the wind of change.

In the best traditions of public watchdogs, community health councils were dogged, and this is a characteristic that often does not win friends. Unimpressed by bland or evasive answers, they continued to ask the awkward question until they were satisfied. This behaviour often raises the hackles of those, who (even if they haven't got anything to hide) are uncertain of their facts, or afraid of being caught out. The daily prayer book of the corporate manager starts with "Lord, let it not be to-day that I get found out", and however able the manager, there is always the risk that a difficult question in one area may open up an oversight or a failure in another. So managers do not like to be cross-examined.

Any machinery (such as Internal Audit) created to question and challenge the manager's decisions, recommendations or reasoning is likely to cause tension. The same is true of a body such as a CHC, which does not go away when its visit is finished, but comes back time and again with a similar purpose. In this context 'manager' can just as easily mean 'clinician' or 'civil servant', with equal relevance. I have said several times that there are managers who enjoy this kind of pressure and find it a stimulant to their performance, but this is not general. Lesser – perhaps more sensitive – executives are going to sense the threat, and will struggle with it. It is these who will be inclined to dismiss the intruder as 'amateur' or 'hostile', and spread the message. Ironically, the same people, confronted with an unenergetic or bland monitoring body will be quick to spot its weaknesses, and stern in their criticism.

It follows that in its dealings with senior Department of Health or NHS staff, any body of a watchdog type is likely at some time to generate negative feelings in a significant proportion of those with whom it deals and a consequent "bad press" for itself even when its conclusions are correct and well thought out. Without labouring this point, CHCs were open to any number of such attacks aimed broadly at their legitimacy or their assumed variability; or politically at their composition, attitudes or motivation; or operationally at the suggestion that while they had the luxury of criticising, it was others who had to take the difficult decisions, and so on. It is said that in this country there is a greater respect for elective democracy than the representative kind, and since CHCs were not elected bodies, they were likely to be categorised as second division players. The fact that they were often quite successful at what they did simply served to exacerbate matters, opening them up to further attack from the NHS and Departmental freemasonry.

Historically, the watchdog role of CHCs undoubtedly sparked many improvements to the quality of local health services and their sensitivity to the needs of their users in every part of the country. Many worthwhile initiatives owed their origin (at least in part) to suggestions from CHCs, and some unsuccessful schemes were withdrawn as a result of their criticism. Where failures came to light, CHCs were at the centre of efforts to deal with them in the interests of patients and their families, and in some cases, timely warnings from the CHC prevented situations from getting out of control. From Normansfield in the mid 1970s to Bristol Royal Infirmary in the 1990s, their discharge of the watchdog role proved how central the independent voice of the users' representative in the NHS was in protecting the public interest.

I have heard stories of CHCs which were less than fully committed to their work, and particularly perhaps, during the long wind-down from July 2000 to December 2003. But my experience has not been of that kind. If asked for a broad assessment, I should want to record my recollection of CHCs as groups of enthusiasts, with both staff and key members putting in far more work than their duties necessitated, and making a contribution to the well-being of their communities well beyond simply their activities as CHC members or employees.

From my own memory, as *well* as from annual reports and accounts given to me, I am able to show extensive evidence of new voluntary organisations set up as a result of CHC or joint CHC/community action; community development work done by CHCs with mothers' groups, ethnic minorities (sickle-cell, thalassaemia etc.) and elderly people; exercises in addiction, mental health and rehabilitation, community care and hospice campaigns from many parts of the country.

This is the sort of work that led Ruth Bucky (former chair of Haringey CHC) to give twenty-three years of her life to the Advisory Group on Alcohol in Haringey, launched originally by the CHC with a small cash grant from Marks and Spencer with one part-time worker based in the CHC office, and still running today.

At the start, this group received help from the Greater London Alcohol Advice Service. Today, it turns over more than £1m per annum, running a day centre and a home-detoxification service; offering advice, counselling and support for the children of alcoholic parents, a return-to-work training centre; bedsitter accommodation and an assessment unit. It also employs Greek and Turkish speaking link-workers in association with the NHS. Its current funding comes from charitable sources, the local authority and the primary care trust. Haringey CHC may now be only a memory, but the initiative it took twenty-three years ago to tackle an unmet local need continues to flourish as a legacy to its community.

The same sort of spirit gave birth to three key civic and social projects masterminded by St Helens and Knowsley CHC: the £2m Willowbrook Hospice; the £7m Millennium Centre and the £1m disabled people's development at Dorothy Street in St Helens. The CHC was able to look with pride at the major changes it generated in the provision of services to the most vulnerable people in its district, and the borough council of St Helens recognised its work by creating Tony Richards, chief officer of the CHC, a Freeman of the borough in 2000.[2] The honour also recognises Tony Richards' personal contribution in active collaboration with voluntary services in the borough throughout the lifetime of the CHC, which he joined as secretary in 1974.

These two instances deserve mention because they illustrate my point exactly. Both of them turn on work done by the community health council, but they equally tell a story of personal effort above and beyond the call of duty; in one case on the part of a CHC member, and in the other by a member of staff. Paul Reynolds had a point when he spoke of CHCs delivering a Rolls Royce to their communities for the price of a Fiesta. The work done by Ruth Bucky and Tony Richards cost the community not a penny, and nowhere in the public service could you find better than that.

I should like to give just one more illustration of CHC enthusiasm that generated a wider community involvement and got things done – in this case both a member and a staff member have starring roles. Win Smith was chair of the CHC in Newcastle-upon-Tyne from 1981 to 1988, and wrote one

---

[2] Tony Richards' work was also recognised in the 2006 New Year's Honours List with the award of a MBE. A similar award was made in the same honours list to Derek Smith for work with disabled people in Rutland, an area in which he was active when CHC Secretary in East Leicestershire many years ago.

of several memoirs commissioned by the council for its final annual report. In common with Ruth Bucky, Win put her mind and heart into services for disadvantaged people in a neglected area – homeless and nomadic – who in many cases were "refused admission to doctors' surgeries because of their dirtiness and smell". Her work, backed by the CHC, eventually resulted in the opening of "a small medical centre on Newcastle's quayside, which did yeoman service in dealing with such distressing complaints as ulcerated feet, bronchitis, and often sheer despair".

The CHC also produced a report on hospital mortuaries under her leadership, having observed that they were often situated in damp or mouldy outbuildings offering no facilities for the bereaved. The outcome of their work was not only that the buildings were upgraded, but that the Newcastle hospitals also began a programme of staff training on the care of the dying, which assured grieving friends and relatives of sympathetic consideration. Win Smith concluded her memoir in these modest and generous words: "in so many fields we did help to bring about change, and did support patients, the public, and the medical and nursing staff at a time when enormous medical decisions were taking place. The CHC was a demonstration of how a non-political and non-sectarian service worked selflessly to benefit the community. I wish its successor every good wish for the future."

Win Smith was blessed in having Vera Bolter as secretary of the council during her term as chair. A wise, thoughtful and determined, though never aggressively pushy person, Vera was the Northern Rock on which Newcastle CHC was built and served it for many years. She too was later honoured (with an MBE) for her public service in the city. Her memoir in the same report deals with the "unglamorous parts of the system", and includes the mortuaries and the GUM clinic, but gives its main attention to the care of elderly and confused people (noting the improvements made during the life of the CHC), and those who in the 1970s and 1980s were known as mentally handicapped. She stressed that services for these patients were not given any priority by the DHA until "We managed to bring them to the top of the agenda by confronting a visiting minister with an open letter which caused him to require the Health Authority to produce a plan forthwith – which they had to do."

A Mental Handicap Management Partnership was then formed, comprising members and officers of the DHA and the city council, an equivalent number of relatives and representatives from voluntary organisations, with Vera "seconded from the CHC to make it work". As time passed, this partnership evolved into different structures, but in its day it was a catalyst for significant change. Vera commented: "It is interesting that now (in 2002) partnership boards for mental health services are being reinvented."

On the same general theme, she spoke of CHC support and help for initiatives seeking to promote a community development approach to health. Community health projects in different parts of the city provided "valuable contacts between the CHC and neighbourhoods where people were unlikely to participate in formal consultations but still needed to have a say about health services". Two of these projects continued to flourish up to the time her memoir was written.

As testimony to her commitment, in addition to her routine work, Vera Bolter was able simultaneously to provide administrative support for local research into maternity services and family planning clinics; to run the "Good Practices in Mental Health" project, and to promote a periodical newsletter for community groups entitled "Health Matters".

None of the people associated with these CHCs would ever suggest that their achievements were in any way exceptional, and "CHCs Making a Difference" contains many examples of the excellent work done in the name of the local CHC in every part of the country. Readers with a long memory will also recall that two pages of the ACHCEW annual report for 1989–90 were devoted to a series of similar sketches of CHC achievements, several of them with overtones of community development. Community development is a very interesting piece of the jigsaw of public interaction with CHCs, and reminds me that one of the first steps I took as a newly appointed CHC secretary in Haringey was to set up regular monthly "information and ideas exchange" meetings with the chief officers of the council for voluntary service and the community relations council, and the community development officer of the borough council.

While listless CHCs were few and far between, the unhappy member, whether elected or appointed, is a familiar figure to anyone who has ever been involved in voluntary activity. CHCs naturally had their share of members who quickly found that this was not what they wanted to do. Most often, these were likely to have come from among the appointees of local authorities who had expected a more directly political function than the CHC offered, or were frustrated by its lack of statutory powers. Nominees from voluntary organisations or from the RHAs may in some cases have had to adjust their own expectations, but this would probably have been within a narrower frame of reference, and thus easier for them to achieve. The evidence from CHC membership records is that the generality of members tended to complete their terms of office, and if lucky, to be reappointed or co-opted, thus in some cases retaining their link with the CHC for many years.

The motivation of CHC members covered a spectrum ranging from idealistic altruism to self-interest: some voluntary representatives, for example, may initially have become members to "do something about" a medical problem or disability affecting themselves or their family. Many of these will have begun to see issues in a broader perspective once they were members, and gone on to play a valuable part in the general work of the CHC, recognising the influence that informed pressure for change can have across the entire gamut of health care, including the area of personal importance to them. Some, obviously, will not have been able to reconcile themselves to the realisation that their own preoccupation was not necessarily that of the entire council, and these may well have resigned. But many informed observers believe that the change of attitude described above was by far the more common reaction.

Rod Griffiths was always a great champion of the 'voluntary' members of CHCs. His observation led him to conclude that the local authority members were often the least effective. If councillors, they were either in positions of power on their authority and preoccupied with its business, or they were in opposition and therefore had little real influence which could benefit the CHC. The 'third way' for councillors was that they were minor members of a majority party, in which case it was probable that they were using the CHC to advance their standing among their fellow members. It was only when local authorities began to appoint people who were not councillors that a more constructive approach to the CHC and its work began to emerge. On the other hand, members from voluntary groups collectively displayed a broad enough sweep of interests to leave the single-issue fanatics isolated, with the effect that they were obliged to extend their range of interests or found themselves frozen out.

According to Rod, the majority of 'voluntary' members came to the CHC with some understanding of the NHS as users, or carers, or spokesmen for either or both. They tended to be activists, and to apply their volunteer enthusiasm to their work as CHC members. He also believed that as they accustomed themselves to the politics of CHC work and interactions, they became adept at identifying the most productive ways forward in any given situation. Coming from no prescriptive political position, they were not tactically hidebound, and were concerned above all with getting a result. Moreover, some of them were very able and had long track records of effective community work. Rod found them a valuable and inventive asset to the CHC, and frequently a powerful and resilient spearhead in negotiations with the authorities.

He also had a good word for the RHA representatives who, he considered, formed a useful balancing component. Some of them, he found, had a wealth of relevant experience, while others had potential, and went on to achieve a great deal. To him, an effective CHC needed to understand the politics of its working relationships, to have an attitude, and the drive to get things done. RHA appointees often proved material in developing these capabilities. Tony Smythe once told me more or less the same thing. He said that it was wonderful how CHCs, through a variety of mechanisms, brought together quite ordinary people and taught them the intricacies of the NHS, so that they in time became experts on their own account.

No review of CHCs would be complete without a reference to those who worked for them, since as very small operational units with equally limited resources, the quality of their staff was central to their effectiveness. In writing this book, I have often drawn on the recollections of former CHC chief officers, and at many stages have laid emphasis on the work of chief officers and secretaries as a body. In the 1990s, however, as CHCs began to take on a broader range of functions, other members of staff with particular responsibilities as project officers, complaints handlers, researchers and so on became increasingly important to the successful running of the council, and the service it gave to its members and the public.

Some of those who talked or wrote to me have hinted that CHCs were too dependant on their staff (especially the chief officer) and that the influence they exerted in policy formation and decision making was too powerful; in short, that the staff managed and steered the whole enterprise. That the paid staff should be influential in any kind of organisation is inevitable. Within the department of health, from ministerial level downwards, influence is exerted by senior civil servants. Health authority and trust members have a similar relationship with their chief officers. Even the most respected health service professionals are influenced by their officials – leaders of the Royal Colleges, the General Medical Council and the BMA listen carefully to the advice of their staff. They expect high quality guidance from their advisers, and the more prestigious the organisation, the greater the pride they take in employing staff of the highest calibre. They too must be open from time to time to the charge that the tail wags the dog, but they do not change their policy as a result, and nor should they. If an organisation wishes to demonstrate its professionalism then it must employ staff of commensurate quality.

This maxim applied with equal relevance to CHCs, and was of greater importance to them, since the entire business of the council had to be done by a small number of people. CHC staff were in day to day touch with all the current issues as well as the papers and the arguments surrounding decisions made and in the making. They dealt on a daily basis with the officers of health authorities and trusts, and were expected to give advice to their members, and to offer opinions on all aspects of their work. They needed to be the best the CHC could afford, and as I have shown, in most cases, were committed and enthusiastic themselves.

The point about CHC staff is that they worked in close partnership with the principal members of their council, and that the input expected of them made each staff member a key component of the machine. From the earliest days of one secretary and one assistant, the staff of CHCs worked above their grading and salary. Where the partnership was successful, the outcome was beneficial both to the council and its community, and there was ample evidence of successful collaboration across the country and the years to refute the jibe that CHCs were 'dictated to by their chief officers'.

The question to which I shall now turn is "were CHCs a good idea?" The history suggests that they were the best on offer at the time, and Jean Robinson's "typically British" comment hit the nail on the head. The big disappointment for CHCs was that they never were able to win the hearts of the population. This was partly due to the lack of resources put into them, and the grudging support shown by successive governments, and at all times by the department of health. There could have been media and poster campaigns. There could have been information on public view in every hospital, clinic, surgery and pharmacy in the country. There could have been features on national and local radio programmes, in the national press and popular magazines. There could have been stickers, squeaky toys, smiley faces and other gimmicks, but there were not. Outside the CHC-related sections of the regional health authorities, it could almost be said that not one single departmental or health service finger was ever lifted with the specific aim of giving publicity to the arrival, existence or activity of CHCs. Proportionately, the Welsh Office was more generous, but the difference was slight.

Of course, there were other reasons too. CHCs were not cars, furniture, chocolates, or washing powder, and could not be marketed like these products. Even if a snappy name could have been found for them, they could never have become a household word. They fell into the same category as many worthwhile public service institutions which, however useful the service they provide, are only of interest to the public when it needs them. The Citizens Advice Bureau (CAB), the WRVS and Age Concern are similar in this respect, and although highly respected nationally, they only touch the public consciousness when they are meeting a need, conducting a campaign or raising money.

The situation for CHCs was rather worse, since they were most closely analogous to the consumer councils of the nationalised industries (which scarcely ever made any public impact) and somewhat less with the regulatory offices which have superseded them. The comparison was not wholly sound since (in this context we can agree) CHCs were 'essentially local bodies', whereas the regulators are national. But ignoring that difference, they too only become interesting when publicly criticising the pricing, compensation, marketing or distribution policy of the industry concerned, and then only directly to individuals personally affected by the policy under scrutiny.

Was there any solution to this problem? If it lay anywhere in the work of CHCs, it had to be in information-giving and the redress of grievances. These were the only 'marketable' functions CHCs had, and had they been given these duties explicitly, they could have been 'sold' popularly in those terms first and foremost. This would have gone some way towards putting them on the map, although it would not have been universally popular, since many CHCs believed that their monitoring and public consultation roles were the more important and constructive aspects of their work. The whole question now is only of academic interest, but the substantive point remains: CHCs were never given any national promotional support beyond what they themselves could manage, and as a result they remained to all intents and purposes unknown among the public at large.

But the idea was good. The concept of a public representative body as a counterweight to the professional and technical megalith of the NHS; a locally situated organism, small but agile, and unequivocally on the side of the people: it ought to have been a winner. And substantially it was. In a ceaselessly changing environment, the CHCs in England lasted for almost thirty years, and when they went, at least five bodies, local and national, had to be created to replace them. The organisation, and cost, of patients' forums,

PALS, ICAS, Overview and Scrutiny committees and the CPPIH is a clear indicator of how much CHCs were worth to the country, and the range and complexity of the work they did on behalf of the public.

It is easy to pinpoint failures on the part of government, or the health service management, or CHCs themselves, as reasons why they were unable to change the face of the NHS, and to do so opens up philosophical questions about the nature of British institutions and even the national psyche. Entering all the adverse conclusions in the debit ledger, and realising what a load they carried on their shoulders, it is amazing how much they achieved. As this book approaches publication, some years after the abolition of CHCs, it is my firm conviction that despite all the brave things said in the NHS Plan regarding the place of patients in the health care universe, nothing like the patient support network of the CHC days yet exists, and perhaps never will.

The evidence I have examined suggests that the momentum for change within CHCs was increasing in the years leading up to abolition. Maybe it was too little and too late, and undoubtedly mistakes were made along the way, but I feel confident in concluding that some of the shortcomings which CHCs recognised in themselves and the way they worked were on the way to being rectified, or at least alleviated, when the blow fell. They had very clearly begun to specialise in the area they regarded as their principal function, and in their willingness to accept minimum operational standards in their chosen role, were equally obviously improving their own performance. They can comfort themselves with the knowledge that they were making progress, and that they left behind a legacy of promise that would never be fulfilled.

But that is not the complete story. I have described some of the achievements of CHCs that outlived their creators, and there are many other memorials to them all over the country. The most important of these are the five thousand members and employees who were still there at the finish, and have taken their accumulated knowledge and experience to other areas of activity where they can be of value to the community in different ways. Their contribution will not be lost, though in many cases, it will no longer be devoted to the public interest in the health service. As for community health councils, they came into the world to fill a gap in an otherwise forbidding structure, fathered by an unenthusiastic government and in England unwillingly fostered by the RHAs; extraneous to the NHS but indelibly linked to it; not greatly loved, but determined to do what was expected of them. They had to fight for every inch of ground they won, and when they did well, their very existence seemed to be endangered as a result.

Underfunded and underrated, they were given only grudging credit for their successes. They were frequently criticised and often condemned, both individually and collectively, on account not of their own faults but of the limitations imposed on them by the statutes and regulations which shaped their work. In the end, they were executed for being no more than what their parents had made them.

If government, the health departments and the NHS had really wanted community health councils to be a success, they could have made it possible. Long life in itself is not a proof of success, and their premature end is perhaps only the inevitable culmination of nearly thirty years of struggle against the odds. Looked at from that angle, the achievements of CHCs and the impact they made on the health service during their lifetime were remarkable.

Conclusion

What now for Public Involvement?

"Nowadays... we know so much more about how to involve people and how to do it well, and those techniques must be vigorously employed, because there's no alternative but for people to feel involved again."

(Ruth Levitt, November 2003)

I commented in the last chapter that the NHS Plan of 2000 envisaged several different organisations carrying out the work pioneered by community health councils. Whether represented within the structure of NHS or local government authorities, or as free-standing groups of activists supported by full-time staff, the interests of the users of the NHS and the public at large are of a relevance that was not fully comprehended thirty years ago, and have an intrinsic potential for engagement and empowerment that cannot be exaggerated.

Health authorities (by which I mean practices, hospitals, trusts and authorities of all kinds and descriptions) have themselves become sufficiently aware of their public responsibilities to improve their information and advice services; to brighten up their reception and waiting facilities, and to adopt realistic practices relating to user comfort and the management of their appointment systems. Doctors and the many other competent professionals now in direct clinical contact with the public are conducting their consultations in a discursive manner, as partners in health care transactions, rather than handing out decisions and instructions. This is a major step forward on two fronts: not just the enhancement of the patient's position in the process, but significantly, equally the front-line involvement of NHS professionals previously seen simply as ancillary to the doctors.

These changes are not the result of the Commission for Healthcare Audit and Inspection (CHAI) inspections, nor league tables or even the work of CHCs; they spring from other changes in the ethos of public services, and *inter alia* the increasing impact of privately-run services on all areas of public activity, which has impressed on the managers of the NHS the necessity for regarding their public as customers rather than simply as pieces of a jigsaw to be slotted in where they belong.

But there are still massive obstacles lying in wait for people needing to use the health services or to enter into a debate with NHS management or professionals over issues surrounding the quality, effectiveness or appropriateness of the treatments and facilities they offer. In the first place, an organisation of the scale of the NHS, designed to deal with an entire population and a complete range of physical, mental and medical conditions at every stage of life and disease, cannot be expected to handle every individual or every set of circumstances with equal proficiency. It is simply impossible to do so.

When the scientific, technical, organisational, administrative, manpower, financial and political considerations that influence the operation of any public enterprise are added in; and when the complexity of the enterprise itself and the possible outcomes of any consultation or treatment are taken into account, it is inevitable that there will be many different grounds for unhappiness, disappointment or dissatisfaction with its performance across the spectrum. Faced with a problem, individual patients, or their relatives or carers may have a mountain to climb to arrive at a conclusion they can find satisfactory to them.

The issues at stake may include the possibility of treatment, the alternatives available, the cost (either to the patient or to the NHS), or the manner or competence of the responsible advisers or practitioners; delays and cancellations; organisational efficiency; quality, cleanliness or general comfort, and perhaps matters outside the absolute control of the persons or hospitals concerned. They may not in themselves be cause for complaint, but they may well have clinical, management or political implications.

And to take matters a stage further, they may equally be of a type that requires a response not just within the health service but in the broader community as well. Such issues will demand not just individual action but a catalyst in the shape of public opinion or community action to deal with them successfully, and this could itself take years to achieve.

For nearly thirty years the additional component in England and Wales was the CHC, and in Scotland and Northern Ireland its local counterparts. With its linkages by establishment and by statute to the health authorities; its membership connections with local authorities and the voluntary sector and its interaction capacity with users of the NHS and the public at large, the CHC did provide the catalyst to make – often small but not infrequently quite important – improvements take place. The role, if not the precise machinery, is still recognised by government and the health service as a significant part of retaining the confidence of the nation and its affection for its megalithic health care machine.

Like everything huge, from stegosaurs to supertankers, the NHS is often slow to respond to change, and takes much time and space to turn itself in a different direction. One thing the present government does realise is that the catalyst is necessary for this function too: like a head- and tail-end nerve centre or bow- and stern-thrusters, the impetus from the public has to be present to ensure that the manoeuvre is finally carried out. But in England, it will not in future be done with the aid of community health councils.

Wales, on the other hand, is a different story, and Scotland lies somewhere between the two. The devolved administrations in Wales and Scotland demonstrated a more level-headed (perhaps pragmatic) approach. There were elements in the political parties in Wales and among the civil servants at the Welsh Office that advocated following the lead given by England, but once the arguments on both sides had been considered and the post-abolition situation in England had been observed, the Welsh Assembly decided not to do away with CHCs in Wales. They remain in existence at the time of writing, and have in fact been given statutory duties in advocacy and the redress of grievances. In addition they have been given new functions in relation to primary health care (notably GP) services, together with the extra resources required to cover this additional workload.

Scottish Local Health Councils faced the same kind of pressure for change as in England, but have followed a more evolutionary path, though the final outcome has been not that much different. LHCs continued in operation until March 2005, when they were transformed into one Scottish Health Council, a single national body with small advisory groups in every health district. Consultation and debate on this issue had been going on for some three years. In a speech to the conference of the Scottish Association of Health Councils in September 2003, Malcolm Chisholm MSP, then the Minister for Health and Community Care in the Scottish Executive, said of the planned new patient participation structure: "For the first time we will have at national level a strong organisation... to support patients and to hold the health service to account in... their delivery of patient focus and public involvement."

Following up this development recently with Patricia Alderson, former chief officer of Shetland Health Council, and a friend from ACHCEW days and later in Shetland, I discovered that the present shape of patient and public involvement in Scotland shares many of the characteristics found in England. It seems the Scottish Executive has followed a path that is in some ways parallel to that south of the border, the result being that there are now no longer any local health councils, but not a great deal else to fill the gap either.

Welsh CHCs, while still alive and flourishing, are under no illusion that their long-term future is secure. Chief officers and others to whom I have spoken had no hesitation in making it plain to me that they have the impression of being under scrutiny from the Welsh Office and would not be surprised if at any time, as Welsh local health boards and NHS Trusts become more and more obviously responsible for monitoring their own quality assurance procedures, a question were to be raised concerning the need for their continuation.

Talking to former Welsh colleagues was a pleasant way of renewing old acquaintances, while at the same time learning something of the events of the past ten years from the Welsh perspective. As my advisers I approached Sandra Owen, chief officer at Swansea, whom I had known when she worked with the late Bill Evans in Cardiff more than twenty-five years ago, and Clive Barnby (Pontypridd and Rhondda), Bryn Williams (Brecon and Radnor, formerly at Merthyr and Cynon Valley) and Emrys Roberts (formerly at South Gwent) whose experience and memories stretched back a similar distance.

All were of the opinion that there was a divergence between the English and Welsh CHCs during the 1990s, which they put down to the increasing volume of health policy formation taking place in the Welsh Office without reference to the DoH and the changing management structures in England, which left the English CHCs heavily preoccupied with matters which were scarcely of even academic interest in Wales.

There was some difference among them as to the extent of the separation. Bryn Williams saw it as a wider gap than the others, believing that CHCs in England were becoming increasingly introverted and self-interested at the time. Devolution was notably empowering for the Welsh CHCs, even though it made little difference to their focus. Clive Barnby and Emrys Roberts agreed that from a CHC position it was part of a continuum; a key point in an evolutionary process. It was from then onwards that they began to accumulate additional powers. But it did not bring about a "sea change" in the relationship with CHCs in England. In Clive's opinion, CHCs in Wales never actively considered separation from England, even though they did advocate statutory status for the Welsh Association.

The government's decision to abolish CHCs in England was a shock, causing anxiety in Wales on account of its implications both for England and for their own hopes of survival. It was generally acknowledged that the presence of Jane Hutt AM, the Minister for Health and Social Services at the time and a former member of Cardiff CHC, was crucial from the CHCs' point of view, since she was supportive and as minister, a highly influential advocate. Emrys was somewhat less impressed with her general ministerial performance, believing she was managed by her civil servants rather than vice versa.

It was broadly agreed that the Welsh CHCs had done what they could to support Donna Covey's rearguard action against abolition, though Bryn made the point that it was in some measure only token support, since they knew at heart that there was little hope of success. They also knew that their future lay in Wales, and that Alan Milburn's NHS Plan decisively separated England from Wales, whatever the outcome of the ACHCEW campaign.

Taking a last look at the past, we discussed the issue of variable quality among CHCs. Clive took the view that it was spurious – "one of the big myths of CHCs repeated so often that even we came to believe it". He added that the activities of CHCs and the services they provided throughout England and Wales were fairly consistent, and no more variable than health authorities and trusts. Emrys, however, was of the opinion that it was a genuine issue in England, where as he described it, once the financial problems of the late 1980s had been overcome, it became possible for the chief officers of CHCs to draw their pay from month to month without doing very much to earn it, and that a number of them were astute enough to do just that!

Turning to the subject of ACHCEW, Emrys, who admitted that he left the front line in 1993 to work in service commissioning, said that in his experience ACHCEW was effective and well regarded. Sandra added that until the end, the Welsh CHCs wanted to hold on to their relationship with the association because of its connections in London, and that they still feel its loss on that account. Bryn's view was that, at any rate towards the end of its life, "in day to day terms, ACHCEW was effectively an English body."

There were differing opinions on what CHCs have become, particularly on the part of Emrys, who regretted that CHCs had been 'condensed' into groups serving several districts from one centre, and the loss of their High Street premises. He felt this reduced their appeal from the public point of view, and that since the Welsh Office is pressuring health boards and trusts to develop quality assurance structures, there is at least the risk that CHCs could appear to be superfluous – with fatal consequences (very much what Patricia Alderson had told me in relation to the changes made in Scotland).

Bryn took up the point, saying that health authority quality assurance can never match the scrutiny of a CHC. While he acknowledged that many NHS professionals work within their conception of the interests of service users, he was positive that the influences of the workplace ensure that this can never be an undiluted patient-view, which only a CHC can provide.

Sandra and Clive elaborated on the local health board/CHC interactions, and the efforts by Local Health Boards to develop PPI Health Forums. They stressed that, contrary to appearances, these initiatives are not cramping the CHCs or infringing their areas of activity. The one point on which they all agreed was a general scepticism about what the future holds.

The machinery created for England in 2002–3 is still in operation. The Commission for Public Participation in Health (CPPIH), though expected to be phased out this year, is still directing operations. At the local level, self-managing Patient Participation Forums have been set up throughout the country to offer their advice and recommendations to the Primary Care Trusts and NHS Hospital Trusts in each location. The Trusts themselves now provide a 'customer service' function in the shape of the PALS (Patient Advisory and Liaison Service) run and promoted by each trust.[*]

Independent Complaints and Advisory Services (ICAS) have been created on county, borough or district-wide bases under the auspices of the CAB or other appropriate organisations, and county or unitary local authorities engage in joint service planning and co-ordination with local NHS Trusts, while their Overview and Scrutiny committees in each case examine the performance of the trust(s) and report their findings to them. In this way, the traditional quadripartite interests of the NHS, the local authorities, the

---

[*] A quotable example of the promotion of the PALS service comes from Evesham in Worcestershire, where the windscreen stickers issued in the local car parks carry an advertisement reading:

"South Worcestershire NHS Primary Care Trust. **Patient Advisory and Liaison Service**. Confidential. Advise and support patients, their families and carers. Provide information on NHS services. Listen to your concerns, suggestions or queries. Help sort out problems quickly on your behalf. Freephone **0800-917-7919**"

voluntary sector and the public are preserved, and the health service continues to receive external advice and nudging from elected or appointed representatives of the public – nowadays termed "stakeholders".

Trusts are also involving them in specific quality-related projects. In 2005, for example, South Warwickshire PCT, in co-operation with the county council and Age Concern, set up a working group to monitor the implementation of the National Service Framework for older people. The group included two 'patient' and two 'carer' members representing the interests of both types of service user in Warwick and Stratford on Avon, the two county districts covered by the PCT.

Many observers have recognised merit in the new monitoring and patient-support structures, remarking that each has its own particular work to do, and can concentrate upon its own purpose and effectiveness, without being prone to diversion by any extraneous issues, since these will be handled by one of its sister organisations (CHCs, having no sister organisations, could fall into this trap and might at any time get caught up in a complex or time-consuming complaint, or the campaign of a local community group, or some broad public health question of social importance but little immediate reference to the local NHS). This is very important in these days, when organisations of all kinds are judged by their adherence to their mission statement and 'message', and there is obviously much virtue in following the prescribed path.

They have also pointed out that personal problem solving and the redress of grievances was never one of the statutory duties of CHCs, even if Frank Dobson did believe that they shone at it, and that as a purpose-built body, there is in ICAS a capability which is potentially revolutionary, since the aggregate experience of complaints handling must in time produce a body of evidence which pinpoints the weaknesses of the NHS and sets clear indicators for change.

Ruth Levitt is one who sees this potential and expresses her opinion in these terms:

"The one avenue that is really powerful and may have been underused in the past is the complaints route. That *par excellence* is where you can be the advocate for particular change, generalising from specific misfortune. In the 1970s and 1980s it was regarded as a rather separate strand of work: there was work in the community generally, and there was individual advocacy, when people had a particular problem. It was naïve to think of these as separate, and maybe nowadays we should be more concerned to generalise from the specific instances of issues that arise from complaints, because it's through those stories you can build up knowledge about what's going wrong, and you can be sure that often it won't be an isolated case or at the least there will be a risk of repetition.

"It is worth thinking about how ICAS coming into place could be the generator of wisdom about change that goes beyond individual cases. Historically the health service has handled complaints badly. It has always struggled with having a properly open, fair and accountable system and has not done well in that respect. I would have thought this might be an area for examination."

The problem about this is that ICAS is being operated by a number of different bodies, working as contractors for the health service in their own geographic areas. This means first, that their contract terms may provide only for them to carry out the local advocacy but not to conduct any analysis of their findings and the evidence uncovered; and second, that there may be some difficulty in co-ordinating the work of all the agencies involved in order to obtain a coherent national picture. But the point is well made, and of all the patient-support functions currently operating, ICAS seems to have the most exciting possibilities (CHCs are performing this function in Wales).

Ruth also has advice to offer to members of Patient Participation Forums. Laying stress on the quality of information obtained by the forum and its members, she says "the better informed you are, and the better you are able to be an advocate for a proposition, the more influential you can be. It doesn't really matter what structure you sit in, because if you are wily and sharp and energetic, you can often find your way around all sorts of structural or organisational obstacles in order to pursue or promote a particular point... especially if you rely on information rather than opinion. The value of informed argument is not to be underestimated." This is sound advice for any deliberative body, and perhaps should be embroidered on a sampler and hung above the door of every patients' forum in the country.

She goes on to suggest that the forums should attempt to master all the current community action techniques and use them with vigour, in order to make people feel involved. The work of a forum is essentially political at a local level, and if it is to make an impact, it has to engage its public (perhaps a somewhat different public for each issue) and stimulate its interest. It is well known that where an issue becomes one of local concern people have no difficulty in getting involved and expressing their views. The forum should therefore be using up to date communication methods and framing issues in such a way that without distortion or over-simplification, people can get to feel that they understand them and can have an influence on their outcome. This equally is good advice to any body seeking to express the viewpoint of its community, and offers forum members the potential for greater day-to-day effectiveness and the forum itself the hope of a long and active life. But there is also a caveat, and they should be aware of it.

It is this: there is a so far unmet imperative for the post-2003 organs of patient and public involvement in the need for some form of national cohesion. What applies to ICAS as a *sine qua non* of realising its potential applies with equal force to patient forums. The changes made by the government consequent on the abolition of CHCs have gone a long way to ensure that their successors are in effect Lord Jenkin's "essentially local bodies", looking inward at the trust or locality to which they respond rather than having a broader perspective and a more inclusive horizon. Unless this situation changes notably, the effect that they can have on the body of the health service is only that of localised pinpricks on a Lilliputian scale, where a concerted attack is essential to a worthwhile result.

Moreover, they are at the mercy of political fashion, in the sense that so long as public participation is seen as a "good thing" they will prosper to a greater or less degree, but fundamentally they are hostages to fortune, and if the wind changes, their future could look questionable, since they are no more likely to make themselves indispensable than CHCs were. Given that up to the present, patient forums and ICAS remain uncoordinated regionally or nationally, other than in exceptional circumstances they have little opportunity to make a national impact. Unless they are able to create some broader coordinating mechanisms, their future could turn out to be brief, painful and undistinguished.

To underline this assertion, as recently as 11 October 2005, a Midlands local paper published an article headed "PPI forums get fresh boost", in which it was reported that the CPPIH had reappointed a local housing association as their Forum Support Organisation for a further year. It went on to say that the association would be supporting eight PPI Forums in its area, and quoted one of its managers as saying that it had been chosen for this work "because we have strong links with many sectors of the community. Our networking skills will help to establish forums... by recruiting local representatives and providing them with administrative and training services that will help them achieve their goals". The article went on to notify the public that the housing association manages more than 12,000 houses across the Midlands, and belongs to a group of companies offering services including finance, training, regeneration and development management in the property field. Readers interested were invited to contact CPPIH for further information.

The first point to note is that the housing association had been reappointed (presumably on a competitive basis) for a one-year contract. This means that the immediate management of the PPI forums is short-term and subject to possible annual change. Secondly, the article tells us that nearly three years after the demise of CHCs, forums are now being established. How have the public's interests been nurtured meanwhile? Third, it is clear that the managing organisation is part of a housing, finance and development conglomerate with only tangential interests in health, and those in the limited arena of individual welfare. Fourth, it covers only eight forums, their neighbours being (presumably) managed by quite different bodies, possibly in quite different areas of business or community activity. In all this, there is nothing suggestive of permanence, co-ordination of effort, or the protection and improvement of the health service in any systematic way. If it means that the horizons of the forums are raised no higher than *ad hoc* tinkering, then the future looks unquestionably bleak.

Moreover, as the article demonstrates, the machinery chosen to manage patient and public participation in at least one substantial part of the Midlands is a further instance of the increasing intrusion of private sector companies into the management and supervision of National Health Service functions, which has been the trend since the NHS Plan was adopted in 2000, and seems to have the wholehearted support of the government. If this is the pattern for the future, then it is perhaps no surprise that Alan Milburn abolished CHCs, since they would undoubtedly have stood out vociferously against privatisation, and above all in their own area of activity.

* * *

I am given to understand that the obvious differences in structure and approach between the present bodies and their predecessors are intentional, in the sense that it was decided to make a clean break between the former style of public representation as practised by CHCs and the new approach favoured by the Department of Health and CPPIH. While I can appreciate the desire to innovate, using the new structures to concentrate on particular functions, it will also be apparent that I believe there was much that was worth preserving from the old regime, and that to abandon it all in the name of modernisation is, on the face of it, astonishingly short-sighted. That is, of course, unless what I have just suggested is in any way accurate. For the present it can be said with some certainty that the potentially ground-breaking features of the new system are no more fireproof than CHCs, and in terms of national capability are significantly less well co-ordinated.

Current government philosophy in relation to public services is that they should be driven by standards. The government itself sets the standards and it is up to the public service to meet them. Whether in transport, education or health, the standards are fixed: waiting times for a train or an operation, the quality of the facilities and the customer service. The key to successful performance is that standards are met, and the means of meeting them are secondary. This is the justification for league tables, for "best value" assessments of public expenditure, for foundation schools or hospitals, and for the involvement of the private sector.

Capital developments in health, education and roads are speeded up by the use of the Private Finance Initiative, which the present government has used as enthusiastically as its predecessor. If the waiting time for an operation is the issue, this in the government's eyes justifies offering the options of a hospital in any part of the country, in the NHS or the private sector, in Britain or abroad. If comprehensive schools are failing to meet standards, they can be scrapped and replaced with city academies. Flexibility and choice are the watchwords, and both apply first and foremost to the providers: any source is acceptable if it helps achieve the government's standards, and providers have the ability to commission what they cannot offer themselves from those who can.

The justification for this attitude in government circles is quite simple: children have to reach certain levels of attainment during each year of their education, and if this cannot be assured through existing schools, then other means must be found. By the same token, those in need of medical care, particularly those with potentially life-threatening conditions, need to be treated quickly and competently, which may mean going outside the NHS. Any individual or the family of any individual whose life or prospects are affected by considerations of this kind is likely to sympathise with this view.

But for others, there are important principles at stake: many people have an intellectual and political attachment to the NHS and to the principle of services freely and equally available at the time of need, and many find the use of public money to purchase private sector services offensive. Others still will argue pragmatically that the use of private contractors is more costly in the long term, and that the steps taken today to create new capital projects are saddling the next generation with expenses it will find hard to afford. The debate can be heated, and there are many angles to it, but it is easier to understand many of the policies pursued and decisions taken by the government since 1997 when this philosophy is recognised for what it is and taken into account.

This is a different kind of radicalism from that of previous Labour governments, and clearly controversial in a new kind of way. On any analysis, it seems that CHCs chimed too closely with the older style, and that the newer organs of patient and public involvement fit better with current thinking. Thus, although in aggregate they are more costly (and probably less effective) than their predecessors, like the PFI schools and hospitals they meet short term "best value" criteria, and are politically more acceptable. How they will fare in the medium to long term is a matter of speculation, but it is difficult to be optimistic.

Instinct and a lifetime's experience place me categorically in the *ancien regime*. With all its shortcomings and against the odds, it kindled the enthusiasm of many wonderful people, carried out much valuable work and achieved more than might ever have been imagined. I am proud to have been part of it, and to pay my personal tribute to all concerned in the shape of this, my contribution to the record.

APPENDIX ONE

Final Report of the Ministerial Advisers on Community Health Councils: March 1975

This report is based on the result of a series of visits. Both Councillor Collis and Lady Marre have first met officers (and in some cases members and chairmen) of each Regional Health Authority. The purpose of the visit was to find out from the establishing authority how they had set about their task, and to obtain information about the Community Health Councils, including the names and addresses of chairmen and members etc. so that the necessary meetings could be arranged. We should like to record that RHAs have made information and accommodation available for meetings, and have left the Advisers free to operate without restriction.

In most regions each adviser has had at least two meetings with CHC chairmen and other members. In the West Midlands, however, only 11 CHCs out of 22 had met by the end of February, and therefore it has been possible to hold only one meeting with representatives of the 11 existing councils. A further meeting will be arranged in April. The arrangements have varied according to the size of region and ease of communication. The advisers have taken part in the seminars arranged for newly appointed secretaries by the King's Fund College, the Nuffield Centre for Health Service Studies, Leeds, and the Department of Social Administration, Manchester University. Both have attended individual CHC meetings, covering about 8% of the total number.

General Observations

During the past seven months we have learned that the role and function of CHCs was not at first understood by many people who undertook to become members. By many it was seen as another outside committee which would only involve interest and some attendance at meetings. As the first year of work has progressed, the desire of CHC members to make a contribution to NHS thinking, their appreciation of the need for training, and work outside council meetings has meant that CHC membership now involves a considerable commitment of time and energy. This needs to be made clear to new members in the future.

The task of "representing the local community's interests in the health service" is necessarily a complex one. "Health districts" may, except in London, be coterminous with local authority boundaries, but it is almost impossible to define the nature of the "community" they are supposed to contain. The organisation of the health service is also complex and it is unusual to find even all the basic services provided within the jurisdiction of the health district; psychiatric, geriatric and mental handicap institutions frequently serve more than one district and are often sited at some distance.

Necessarily in these first months CHCs have concentrated on learning about the services provided by the NHS, and on the practical problems of arranging for accommodation, agreeing a budget, and finding a secretary. The majority of CHCs now have their own office premises, but others are experiencing great difficulty in operating without a base. This affects contact with the public, publicity, and general development. Some CHCs have accepted health service accommodation where it is suitable. Others have found homes in local authority premises, shops, or commercial offices. In the absence of guidance, regional or area authorities have taken very different views on what rentals can be approved. On the whole, CHCs have opted for modest premises, and are content to hold their public meetings elsewhere.

In the first instance CHCs had difficulty in understanding that they must prepare and negotiate their own budgets. This is now better understood and in general CHCs are satisfied. There is however a wide discrepancy in the amounts negotiated and actual allocations vary from £6,500 pa. to allocations for 1975/76 of £15,000. This cannot be accounted for solely in terms of rents and travelling expenses. We believe that some CHCs are underfinanced. They all seem to have a very responsible attitude to public expenditure, and are concerned not to use resources which could be used for patient care.

The contribution which will be made by the secretaries has only just begun to appear. We must report that many CHC chairmen felt that the NHS appointment procedure which was almost universally adopted was both cumbersome and inappropriate. What is clear is that the secretaries are generally of high quality, and while some have useful NHS experience others come from research, journalism, the services and a wide range of occupations. Their introductory seminars have served to give them a sense of group identity, and many are meeting to discuss their work with each other. On the status of CHC secretaries, some regions have placed all secretaries on PAA scale. Others have appointed at two levels, PAA and SAA, depending on the population of the district. This is not in many cases reasonable since the type and amount of work is not necessarily less. It was felt in some areas that the grade of secretaries had been decided at too early a stage. Now that most secretaries are in post and the workload is becoming clear, there should perhaps be a review of the grades to see whether there is a case for placing all secretaries on PAA grade. Secretaries need adequate support. Some regions have approved the appointment of assistants on the Higher Clerical grade. This seems appropriate, and we recommend that this should be the general practice.

Some CHCs have obtained more publicity than others. Where CHCs have been unable either to get a secretary or premises, the amount of publicity has been very limited. Some RHAs have been very useful in assisting CHCs to become known to the public and other parts of the National Health Service mainly through the services of their specialist officers. A number of CHCs have designed and provided attractive posters and leaflets. These are now being circulated and as a result the amount of enquiries from the general public is increasing. In rural and small town areas, CHCs have made an effort to distribute leaflets widely and the impact is noticeable. In cities the use of the local authority papers and newsletters has also generated some interest in the work of CHCs. We hope this will be extended to other parts of the country. CHCs are beginning to use local radio, and this too will, we hope, provide a link between the public and the CHCs.

CHCs have yet to find out how to consult their constituents effectively. Some may wish to use survey techniques. This will be possible if they can get adequate professional guidance both locally and (when it exists) from a central CHC organisation. We have encouraged CHCs to make contact with local universities and polytechnics. They may then get long-term research undertaken by a PhD candidate. In the short term they may get advice from the staff and practical assistance from students in carrying out consumer surveys. Others may wish to test consumer opinion "at the point of sale", i.e. by interviewing people in hospitals and clinics or by meeting groups of all kinds from Women's Institutes and Old People's Clubs to local branches of BASW. Those CHCs who have attempted such consultation have found considerable public interest is aroused. One CHC in Northumberland* after arranging to send speakers to various local groups and providing local publicity had 75 members of the public at their next CHC meeting. Hospital closures or change of use have precipitated discussions with the public, and we hope that it will be possible for early experience of this kind to be described for the benefit of CHCs elsewhere.

CHCs are concerned that primary medical care, although within the general responsibility of the AHAs [Area Health Authorities], is largely outside their terms of reference because of the independent contractual relationship between GPs, dentists, pharmacists, opticians and the Family Practitioner Committee (FPC). They see how they can help patients who wish to make a formal complaint about a breach of contract, but not how they can cope with general complaints about insufficient GPs in the district, unsatisfactory appointments, or deputising services. We have advised them to discuss their problems with the GP member of the DMT and if possible with the administrator and chairman of the FPC. Future progress will depend on the tact of the CHC, and the willingness of others to co-operate. We hope that FPC administrators will find it possible to forge good working relationships with the CHC and its secretary. If problems cannot be resolved the National Council may later wish to consider the matter.

During the past seven months we have noticed some change in the attitude of CHCs to certain of the proposals in "Democracy in the Health Service". Nearly all would now welcome the opportunity to send one representative (usually

---

* Northumberland CHC was the only CHC in Northumberland, and it is likely that it was the one to which reference is made in the report. However, the Metropolitan Borough of North Tyneside is situated on the northern bank of the River Tyne, and comprises a number of towns and villages which had formerly been part of the County of Northumberland. It is thus possible, though improbable, that the reference might in fact be to North Tyneside CHC.

chairman or vice-chairman) to AHA meetings with 'observer' status – that is, able to receive all papers and able to speak but unable to vote. They tend to reject the original proposals of either concurrent membership or "secondment" to the AHA. One region has suggested a member with 'observer' status on the FPC.

Finally we would wish to make known the wish of many CHC members to see the original term of office extended in some way. The most sensible and acceptable suggestion is that 1974/75 should be seen as a 'shadow' or 'running in' year. The very considerable difficulties in establishing a completely new organisation have meant that it is only now that most CHCs are starting to work effectively. Changes in 1977, 1979 etc. would be generally acceptable. It would also reduce strain on other NHS authorities to postpone the complicated process of establishment for one year, by which time reorganisation would be further advanced.

Arrangements for establishing the CHCs

The experience of both advisers is that every RHA has tackled this task in a different manner. Both the Regulations and the Circular have been capable of different interpretations. The results have been better than might have been expected although in some county districts some geographical areas are under-represented and on the voluntary side some important community interests have been omitted. Trades Councils and immigrants' organisations are cases in point in certain districts. The greatest difficulty arose on the selection of representatives of voluntary organisations. We have prepared a paper making a number of detailed suggestions about the procedure which we hope will assist the Department in drafting the necessary circular for the next round. Some CHCs have suggested that they should be responsible for the whole procedure in the future but this is not generally acceptable or desirable.

They could have a very useful function if they were to be responsible for compiling a list of voluntary organisations who are interested in the CHC and who wish to put forward a nominee to the CHC as well as an even fuller list of appropriate voluntary organisations in the area who do not wish to put forward a candidate. We feel that this might relieve some of the strain on the RHA staff and would be appropriate to the CHC.

1. Total Membership

- **Size of the CHC:** Within the range of possibilities open to them, RHAs have adopted different policies on the number of members of CHCs. Some (e.g. the North Western Region) have favoured the maximum number (30) for each CHC, feeling that this would give the widest opportunity for representation of different interests. Other regions (notably South West Thames) have taken the view that they should work from the basis of about a membership of 24 to allow room for later modifications. They, in common with many others, have taken as guidelines for increasing the number, the size of population, the geographical spread, and the complexity of Health Service institutions. Individual CHCs have rarely questioned the number fixed.
- **Residence qualifications:** Some CHCs have a disproportionate number of members living outside the district. CHC members are generally in support of the proposition that members should be resident in the district they represent. There are, however, problems in the large conurbations if this were to be too rigorously enforced. Members who are employed in the district, notably those concerned with social welfare in the widest sense, often have much to offer. Members should, however, have a substantial stake of interest in,

and knowledge about the district. Knowledge of hospitals alone is not enough.
- **Double membership:** If residential qualifications are broadly accepted, then it is clear that no one (whether representing a local authority or other body) can be a member of more than one council as is the present case.

2. Local Authority Members

Where there has been considerable local government reorganisation there have been some problems in agreeing how the local authority membership should be divided, but generally nominations have come forward without difficulty. Some local authority nominees have found that it is difficult to fit in their CHC responsibility, and have resigned. CHCs have however greatly benefited from the members who are on relevant local authority committees (e.g. Social Services). For the moment this seems a more useful link than the Joint Consultative Committees which in some areas have not yet met. Some CHCs have asked to be represented on the JCC as full members. Some have been granted 'observer' status. This is useful as the committee is not open to the public.

3. Representatives from Voluntary Organisations

The method of selection was varied and open to criticism. It is however easier to criticise than to put forward practical alternatives. As stated above, we have made some detailed proposals for the Department's consideration.

4. RHA Appointments

We would suggest that RHAs should be encouraged to be flexible in their use of this category. Some RHAs have been rather hospital-minded in their selection of candidates, and have given insufficient thought to filling gaps in community representation. Others have been most imaginative and have found candidates with valuable experience, skills and enthusiasm. This category should not be confined to the specific groups referred to in Circular HRC(74)4.

Training

CHC members have undertaken training with enthusiasm when it has been available. The preliminary seminars have been seen by them as being a means of clarifying their role and learning to work as a group during the interim period without staff or premises. Where no regional arrangements were made, progress has tended to be slower and later work less effective. Plans will need to be made for seminars for new members when membership changes, and perhaps for opportunities for those who missed the first round, or wish to increase their skills.

The three centres concerned with the induction courses for secretaries have in their very different ways set standards and made a significant contribution to the future work of CHCs and their staff. We hope that in-service training of secretaries will continue, and that sufficient resources will be available to enable them to attend seminars and other suitable courses.

Methods of working

CHCs now have either a formal structure of sub-committees or working groups which can come to an end as circumstances change. Some CHCs have linked the visiting of NHS establishments with the work of these groups rather than 'rota' visiting. This seems to focus the visit satisfactorily and distinguishes it from the AHA members' visit. Most CHCs find some sort of executive committee useful: to discuss, for example, what questions they wish to put to the District Management Team at the open council meeting, and to sort out administrative and organisational matters. Some CHCs have a regular open forum at the end of their meetings. This is a useful means of attracting public attendance.

Relationship with other health service authorities

1. The RHA

CHC members were first aware of the RHA, its members and its officers. Some RHAs have been skilled in giving support, advice and help without attempting to create a relationship of dependence. Some have also encouraged the CHCs to use their specialist officers (e.g. PR staff) or special facilities such as a library. Others have been less forthcoming. We were surprised to find that not all RHAs circulated their minutes to CHCs.

2. The DMT and the AHA

The relationships between the CHCs and their DMTs are, on the whole, developing satisfactorily on a personal level. Once initial suspicions have been dispelled, the DMTs tend to regard the CHCs as allies in obtaining a fair share of resources for their district. The contact between the AHA and its officers, and the FPC and the CHCs is still often tenuous.

3. Relationships through information flow

While we have accepted an assurance of good relationships at their face value we have endeavoured to use the provision of information as an indicator of the real degree of co-operation. CHCs are unable to perform their work properly if they are not clear about the thinking and plans of the other authorities. We have enquired from CHCs about the provision of AHA agendas and minutes and other reports. While many CHCs are receiving two or more copies of the full papers and make them available to members in the CHC office we have, to our surprise, found CHCs who have not yet received even the minutes of the open part of the AHA meeting. DMT minutes and notes are less frequently available. In one region only are they provided as a matter of course. There is no evidence we have heard to show that CHCs are not using this confidential material responsibly. We believe our enquiries into this have encouraged CHCs to ask for more information, and in most cases to receive it.

We should like to emphasise that CHCs can only fulfil their role if sufficient information is forthcoming from all sources, i.e. statistics, circulars, minutes, agendas and reports. This is important if they are to give a constructive view on plans, closures etc. In principle we believe that confidential papers should be available also, but we recognise that this raises problems which need to be very carefully handled. For the moment Hospital Advisory Service reports are not available. If their scope or content were ever to be changed we suggest that CHCs should receive them. In any case the CHC concerned should be notified of the recommendations.

4. Relationships involved in planning

CHCs need to know how their Health Care Planning Teams are to work if they are to make a significant contribution to their thinking. This can be through individual membership or by contributions from the working groups. This still needs consideration. CHCs should be informed of the teams' terms of reference at an early stage. They can then arrange to test consumer opinion on the issues involved.

5. Consultations about closures and change of use

It is clear that much work will need to be done on what is involved in, and what is meant by such consultation. One CHC has complained that it was completely excluded from informal consultations and only consulted formally about a closure when proposals were already firm. This seems to have been the result of a misunderstanding of a circular by the health authority. Some have complained that CHCs were seventh on the list of bodies to be involved in informal consultations. Others have complained that their AHA has seen consultation as a once-for-all procedure on any one issue, and not as a continuing dialogue. Consultation about closures has brought this issue to the attention of CHCs and they are concerned that their role is not fully understood. As one secretary put it "consultation is not something that can be turned on and off like a tap".

Complaints

The fear that CHCs would release a flood of individual complaints has been proved completely unfounded. On the contrary, CHCs have yet to make sufficient contact with the public to enable them to come forward with confidence. We believe that whenever possible CHC secretaries and members should assist members of the public to put their complaints in writing. With the consent of the complainant a copy should be kept at the CHC office. CHCs should (if possible) arrange that a copy of the health authority's reply is sent to them. This will enable them to monitor complaints with some accuracy. Most CHCs have agreed a procedure for processing the complaints received with their DMTs, i.e. that all complaints should be referred to the District Administrator. As they increasingly 'go public' CHCs will need to learn from each other how best to encourage the public to come forward with complaints, criticisms and suggestions. Few CHCs have yet helped complainants make contact with the Health Service Commissioner. Some CHCs have started advice centres or 'surgeries' to deal with complaints from the public. So far the numbers attending these sessions have been very small. We would suggest that CHCs should try to establish that they are opening such a centre or surgery in the right place and at the right time before involving themselves in this use of their resources. This service is time consuming but is helpful and appropriate if in the right place. It needs proper preparation and adequate publicity if it is to work. It might not perhaps be the first priority in terms of time available to CHC members in spite of its superficial attractions. A more positive approach to groups at risk might be preferable.

Two CHCs have asked about the role of the CHC in a private inquiry set up by a health authority. One CHC has asked for the right to appoint an observer who will be concerned to watch over the patients' interests. The North Western Regional Association of CHCs has passed a resolution calling for an active involvement in the inquiry itself. The role of the CHC may become clearer when the government's views on the Davies Committee recommendations are available.

Regional Organisations

A variety of regional organisations are springing up. Some are joint organisations of members and secretaries; some are for members only; some for secretaries. At this stage a variety of approaches is fruitful. Where a formal constitution has been adopted there has been provision made for any necessary changes following the establishment of any national organisation.

Steering Committee for a National Council for CHCs

Most CHC members would like some central services provided by an organisation under their own control. A minority would defer consideration of this for another year. There is general agreement that information, guidance to publications and the opportunity to exchange ideas are needed first, then central publicity services, and finally a platform from which CHCs can put forward on a national basis the views of the consumer. They unite in wishing to have a non-bureaucratic organisation with a minimum of formality and with a small but good professional staff. A steering committee is in the process of being formed which will include some secretaries as well as CHC members. It will make recommendations which will, we hope, clarify ideas about function, representation and finance. As the prospective chairman and vice-chairman we intend that the members of the steering committee will have ample opportunity to consult both CHC members and staff so that the committee's recommendations can be broadly based. We believe that any national council set up as a result of such recommendations would enable individual CHCs to be more effective, and would assist them in their wish to ensure that the maximum of the resources available goes to a health service which will be more responsive to consumer needs.

(Signed)
Mary Marre   Ken Collis

March 1975

APPENDIX TWO

Ministerial Statements

I decided to approach every health minister in office during the period 1972–2000 who had had responsibility for community health councils as part of his or her area of ministerial interest. This appendix summarises the replies I received and includes my own comments on what they had to say. Patrick Jenkin, Frank Dobson and Roland Moyle gave me detailed interviews, and in a number of other cases, the written answers were enlarged upon by telephone.

Initially I wrote to twenty-two former health ministers, and received replies from most of them. Some were of the "thank you for your letter" variety, but the majority were quite helpful. Early Secretaries of State were difficult to come by. Sir Keith Joseph, Barbara Castle and David Ennals are now dead, as is Gerry Vaughan, the parliamentary secretary at the time of "Patients First". I succeeded in getting comments, in some cases brief and in others detailed, from Patrick Jenkin, Kenneth Clarke, Stephen Dorrell, Frank Dobson and Alan Milburn.

Among ministers below Secretary of State level, the most interesting contributions came from Michael Alison (Conservative government 1970–74), David Owen and Roland Moyle (Labour government 1974–79), and from Edwina Currie, Tom Sackville and John Bowis (Conservative junior ministers between 1988 and 1996).

I did not contact any of the junior ministers who have served in the government since 1997, taking the view that the years 2000–2003 would be reasonably fresh in the minds of many of my readers, and that the statements made by Frank

Dobson and Alan Milburn would suffice. I also wanted to avoid the risk of placing them in a difficult position by asking them to comment on questions that may have been controversial within the ministerial team and might still have a possible impact on their parliamentary prospects.

Rita Lewis wrote to Earl Howe (Conservative spokesman in the House of Lords at the time) who replied just as constructively as he spoke to the ACHCEW conference in 2002. Michael Alison, who as junior minister to Sir Keith Joseph led the NHS Reorganisation Bill through its committee stage in the Commons in 1973 provided a unique insight into the way in which CHCs were progressively strengthened during that period.

I am greatly indebted to all these former ministers and spokespeople for their helpful input, and for the time and trouble they took in making it.

* * *

Lady Mary Marre recalls that David Owen was the driving force behind the appointment of the two ministerial advisers on CHCs to Barbara Castle, Secretary of State at the time. David (now Lord) Owen, who later became leader of the Social Democratic Party (SDP), made no reference to this in his comments to me. He did say that when Labour took office in 1974, the appointed day for the implementation of the 1973 NHS Reorganisation Act was imminent and the process could not at that stage be halted. The government was obliged to mould what it had, despite "substantial criticism of the structure we inherited". He added that he gave all the encouragement he could as a minister to the CHC network, and that he had no regrets for doing so.

In his book *In Sickness and in Health* published in 1976 at about the time he left the DHSS, David Owen made the powerful statement on community health councils that in part inspires this present work:

251

"The decision to establish community health councils will probably be looked back on by social historians as the most significant aspect of the whole of the NHS Reorganisation Act 1973. For the first time there exists a strong consumer body to both criticise and champion the NHS."

Dr Owen was not shy of appearing before CHC audiences, and spoke at many events around the country, to the point where he was acknowledged as being a high public profile minister. One such occasion was in October 1975, shortly after the first interim report of the DHSS Resource Allocation Working Party (RAWP), when I was secretary of Haringey CHC. We organised a conference to draw attention to the state of local health services and the potential impact of the RAWP-inspired 'rationalisation' and other changes taking place in the district.

The conference, entitled "Health in Haringey" was intended to present a comprehensive picture to professionals and public alike, and to let them see how decisions to reduce or alter services taken by the AHA or the local authority could have widespread and sometimes unexpected repercussions. The objective was to impress on decision makers the need to take the furthest reaches of their implications for the community into account before recommending or agreeing to any changes, however dire the circumstances.

Invitations were sent to the members and officers of the area health authority and the borough council; to the DMT, the FPC, hospital doctors and GPs. They were also extended to the NHS and local government unions; voluntary groups active in the borough, and the local press.

The event took place at Haringey Civic Centre and was chaired by the Mayor of Haringey, Cllr. Daisy Cunningham, who was a member of the CHC. To ensure the success of the occasion, we asked David Owen to be the keynote speaker.

He came, and spoke, weaving the theme of the conference into a statement of the government's objectives and the financial constraints it faced, which was extensively reported locally and in *CHC News* the following month. The conference was well attended by the invitees, and produced much useful information and advice for participants. It enhanced the standing and reputation of the CHC, but in reality, probably did little more than to sharpen up the performance of managers in preparing and presenting proposals for rationalisations, redeployments, closures and changes of use to their members.

One of the steps Dr Owen took by way of encouragement to CHCs was the appointment of the ministerial advisers. It was certainly a substantial step. So far as I can ascertain, it was the first and only time a formal means was established to find out from CHCs themselves what it was that they wanted and needed to carry out the duties laid down for them, and to go some way to meet their wishes. The question was one that over the years CHCs and ACHCEW frequently, and sometimes acrimoniously, asked themselves. One of the criticisms levelled at regional health authorities in the 1990s when they established performance reviews for CHCs and their staff was that they took no steps to find out from their respective councils exactly what they were doing and what resources and other encouragement they needed to do it effectively.

The strong commitment expressed in the quotation from his book seems to have grown less vigorous in the intervening years. David Owen's final word to me on CHCs was that they "did introduce some worthwhile elements to consumer choice. But there was great variation in performance and a lot depended on the quality of the secretary". Community health councils' final word on David Owen might well, on the basis of his actions in 1974 and 1975, have been to place him among the righteous in their own hagiography.

When David Owen left the DHSS to go to the Foreign Office and on to greater things in 1976, Roland Moyle was his successor as Minister of State. This was relatively a quiet time for CHCs, which although engaged in trench warfare with their area health authorities – and sometimes with doctors too – were at least popular with ministers, and were consolidating their position in their own districts. David Ennals was Secretary of State, and was reported to be taking a keen interest in their development and the way they were settling in alongside the new NHS structure. Addressing the one-day conference of ACHCEW in London in September 1978, he spoke warmly of the work of CHCs and promised access to family practitioner committees to those as yet denied. Not everything was perfect, as *CHC News* pointed out in its Christmas message to Mr Ennals that year, but it seemed as if the thoughts of government and CHCs were running in a similar way.

I asked Roland Moyle for his reflections on community health councils at twenty-five years' distance. His first point in reply was that he still favours the existence of separate bodies in the health service whose task is to represent the interests of the public, and have no management role. He considered this good democratic practice, and was convinced that it brought unlooked-for benefits in that the members developed a knowledge and expertise which permeated into both NHS and public thinking, presenting a challenge, and if used properly, a useful tool for ministers in testing new policies or ideas.

His own immediate link with a CHC was through his London constituency of Lewisham. He was impressed by the helpfulness of Lewisham CHC and by the hard work and ability of Celia Pyke-Lees, chief officer at the time. While Mr Moyle took the line that some representations from CHCs in relation to hospital closures or changes of use were less constructive than they might have been – no instances were quoted – he did acknowledge that the majority were closely argued, and that in all cases, "the councils stuck up for their local hospitals". He added that when he received deputations from CHCs, "they always made a very good, constructive, sensible case".

Patrick Jenkin had told me that at that time, when he was shadow Secretary of State, he received regular hostile reports on CHCs from consultants and hospital managers. When I asked Roland Moyle if he had the same experience, he replied, "No. I think it was assumed that the government was in favour of CHCs and that there was little point in lobbying us." This is possibly true, but it seems to me more likely that those who wanted CHCs abolished (who were probably a very small minority among their own professions) were also inclined to bring their discontents to opposition spokesmen, who in their view would be more likely to make use of them as weapons, and as subsequent events showed were correct in that assumption.

Roland Moyle had mixed feelings about local authority representation on CHCs, commenting that, in his opinion, it was not a tremendous success. He was rather more enthusiastic about the voluntary members, stating that the way they learned to work with one another and how to handle the politics of a situation was good. From his point of view, the great bonus was getting ordinary members of the public involved in the health service, taking their knowledge back to their streets and community centres, and using it to inform local discussion. Variable performance didn't seriously trouble him. He saw it as a fact of public life, and "couldn't say that it ever obtruded on me and made me worry about it".

My final question to Mr Moyle was about what he would produce if asked to reinvent a consumer body for the NHS. He answered quite firmly that left to himself he would come up with something similar to a CHC. Regarding the election process, he saw no need for direct election, adding that while one might describe the membership of CHCs as 'guided democracy', it was "much more democratic than that of health authorities and trusts".

* * *

The period of the 1974–79 Labour government was one during which the proponents of private medical practice in the NHS felt their position under threat, particularly at the hands of Barbara Castle and David Owen. They therefore looked to Margaret Thatcher and the Conservative opposition as an apologist for their position and a parliamentary line of defence. They found a willing ally, and the opposition spokesmen built what Patrick Jenkin described as "a very good rapport with the consultants... [and] ... a large number of leading doctors". These doctors were not simply concerned with the perpetuation of private practice; they were also up in arms against the existence and the activities of the new community health councils, viewing them as 'agents of subversion' and 'totally hostile to the medical profession'.

It is difficult to reconcile this extreme attitude with the actual behaviour of CHCs; the innumerable CHC reports praising the efforts of individual consultants working in highly unfavourable conditions, and the alliances formed with medical professionals in all parts of the country to improve the situation of different wards, departments and specialties in their districts which were characteristic of CHCs in the early days. It is also difficult to believe that the Conservative leadership could have been taken in by this shrill polemic and ignored the majority of doctors who either welcomed the new element or were prepared to live with it. Yet Lord Jenkin told me categorically that the question mark over the existence of CHCs in "Patients First" was the upshot of regular discussions with these consultants, and similarly minded administrators.

If this explanation for the "Patients First" attack on CHCs seems, to put it mildly, less than fully convincing, Patrick Jenkin quickly became a convert to their cause. In his speech to the special meeting of ACHCEW held in the Wembley Conference Centre on 15 February 1980, the Secretary of State set out six arguments in support of CHCs as well as elaborating on some of the more hostile comments that had been made during the consultation period. Looking back on that speech more than twenty years later, he said that the DHSS had "rightly accepted the bulk of the arguments I spelt out as to why they should be retained... and I have never regretted that decision".

In similar vein, looking at the government's action in 2000 by way of comparison, he had this to say:

"Tony Blair wants to control everything. CHCs were seen as a thorn in the government's flesh, and therefore they had to go. We didn't see it like that. We saw them as local bodies, conducting a dialogue, sometimes quite fierce, but conducting a dialogue with local health services... individually and collectively. I think that was right... and I'm sorry that they won't be there [any longer]."

As Secretary of State, Lord Jenkin's vision of the NHS was one of a consultant-led and hospital centred service, with the consultants the top dogs, with everyone else employed to support them in their work. All the administrative and nursing staff, right to the highest level, came into this category. He believed in an appointed board membership, both regionally, and at the operational level. Community health councils fitted into his scheme of things, because in that kind of structure, it became necessary to have a patient/public representative counterweight.

In his MBA dissertation on the abolition of CHCs, Peter Walsh, a former Director of ACHCEW, labelled the intrusion of a minister into the framing of legislation in line with his own personal opinions as counter-democratic, and flagged the case of CHCs as a cause for more general concern. My experience has been that ministerial predilections feature more frequently in the shaping of legislation than one might care to think. Peter may be interested to know that this seems to have happened to CHCs once before, since by Lord Jenkin's admission, apart from the extremist administrators and consultants who were lobbying him at the time of "Patients First", Margaret Thatcher was "pretty hostile" and Gerry Vaughan, his junior minister, totally opposed retaining them (he was also extremely obstinate).

Roland Moyle remarked to me that it was Gerry Vaughan who had led for the government on "Patients First", and when I pointed out to him that unless the House was alert, an item of this kind in a white paper or bill could go through unchallenged, his only comment was "Well, we were very attentive on the day."

Kenneth Clarke was the last minister I dealt with while at ACHCEW, and we had what might be called a seesawing relationship – shifting personally and politically as the pressures of the day or the stance of our respective organisations dictated. Mr Clarke was Minister of State at the time of the axing of *CHC News*, and rejected requests from ACHCEW and numerous CHCs to reconsider that decision. He still came willingly to Sheffield to speak at the ACHCEW conference in 1983 although the die had by then been cast, and he could not in the circumstances expect a rapturous reception from the assembled CHC members. From Mr Clarke's point of view, it is quite possibly a teaspoonful of water that went under the bridge many years ago, and he cannot now remember. From CHCs' point of view the impact of his decision at the time was akin to a family bereavement.

He responded to my approach with typical directness, taking me back to the passage of the 1973 NHS Reorganisation Act when he was government whip on the committee considering the Bill. He restated the generally accepted position that community health councils were added to the Bill as something of an afterthought in response to complaints that Sir Keith Joseph's proposals were too much focussed on management changes and had no element of patient advocacy in them. While it seems to overlook the 1971 consultation, the 1972 white paper and the initial wording of the Bill, the opinion expressed by Mr Clarke is probably based on the rapid evolution of the concept of CHCs during the committee stages of the Bill and the mythology which grew out of it.

In speaking of advocacy, it is clear to me that he meant advocacy in the broader sense, because he went on to say:

> "I think the intention at the time was that CHCs should form local consumer groups, who would make representations to health authorities on behalf of local residents about detailed aspects of the local delivery of services. They were expected to act in the way in which an ombudsman or the complaints procedures of health authorities would be expected to function in 2003."

i.e. advocacy in the sense of taking the patient's part in dealing with specific complaints, and in the general sense of presenting the views of its community on local health service performance to the authorities concerned as a permanent function.

In Kenneth Clarke's opinion, CHCs have varied "very widely from place to place" in the way they have tackled their functions. Some of them, he acknowledges, were quite effective as local consumer groups, making an input into the work of their local health authorities with the aim of making the service more responsive to the needs of users. This is clearly the role to which he still sees CHCs as having been best suited. As far back as 1982, at a meeting with the officers of ACHCEW, he assured us that on issues of consultation, the contributions coming from CHCs were thoughtful, well prepared, and valuable to him as a minister.

He believes it was unfortunate that the precise role of community health councils was never clearly spelt out. This made it possible for some, in his view, to become 'pressure groups on policy' and more inclined to be influenced by staff interests within the NHS than by patients and the public. Any form of direct election to CHC membership would, as he saw it, have created a real risk of the control of individual CHCs being seized by unrepresentative pressure groups or the trade unions.

Adhering to Patrick Jenkin's doctrine of "essentially local bodies", Mr Clarke levels a similar criticism at ACHCEW, claiming that it "became a vehicle of the more [politically] active CHCs and at times tried to become an active participant in debate about policy towards the health service". The result of this was that relationships between the government and ACHCEW (and even some CHCs) could become "very competitive and party political". Because of this, Mr Clarke preferred to keep his dealings with CHCs as far as possible in the arena of the quality of service and patient-based issues.

Following Kenneth Clarke's analysis towards its logical conclusion, the longer term seeds of disaster can be seen to have lain in this politicisation of CHCs, since the asperity of the interface with government was not eased by the election of New Labour in 1997. In an unusually candid and interesting observation on the final abolition of CHCs arising from this point, he added:

"The New Labour government obviously began to take the same view as myself, and in a rather typical Blairite way decided to abolish them, which I do not think we would ever have dared to do."

This echoes Patrick Jenkin's "thorn in the flesh" comment pretty closely, and while both statements are obviously rooted in party political opposition to the Blair government, they are consistent with a number of suggestions put to me from other quarters as to the real reasons for abolition of CHCs under Labour's NHS Plan.

Kenneth Clarke has the reputation of being intelligent, forthright, unconventional and iconoclastic. As a Conservative MP and minister over the years he has often demonstrated his personal courage and independence of mind. Many of the people I spoke to in the course of writing have spoken well of him, and it is likely that the majority of former CHC members and staff would agree with that judgment. Community health councils were created to a pattern that ensured a membership of politically articulate people with strong and forceful opinions and a measure of NHS expertise. I am absolutely certain that if Mr Clarke had found himself a member of a CHC, he would have expressed his own views as vigorously as anyone, and I am disappointed that he deplores an equal determination and commitment on the part of those who *were* members. I am not sure that he liked CHCs as much as the people in CHCs liked him.

The final Conservative Secretary of State before the 1997 election was Stephen Dorrell, who succeeded Virginia Bottomley in 1995, and was thus in office at the time of the Insight consultants' report on the future role of community health councils and the debate which followed. Mr Dorrell had already done battle with CHCs as junior health minister in 1990 and, uniquely among top politicians, had attended a meeting of the standing committee of ACHCEW to put his own views, and hear those of the regional CHC representatives. Toby Harris believes the earlier skirmish was not a major run-in. In his opinion, Stephen Dorrell's involvement was "a positive thing" and "the dialogue we built up with him when he was Parliamentary under-

Secretary meant that when he was Secretary of State, we actually had a stronger relationship with him than might otherwise have been the case.

Mr Dorrell's response to my enquiry was brief and to the point, and is best quoted as written:

> "Although I recognise the increasing importance in health care delivery of the consumer viewpoint, and I also recognise the tremendous commitment of active members of CHCs in trying to provide this perspective, I am bound to say that I do not believe that the CHC system proved to be an effective way of delivering it.
>
> "The experience of the patient is inevitably highly personal. Patient collectives, therefore, inevitably find themselves sidetracked into issues of health management and health policy rather than focussing directly on the patient perspective. In a word, they tend to become 'too expert' – insiders, not outsiders.
>
> "I am not, therefore, in favour of trying to reinvent CHCs, but I am very mindful of the fact that the problem they were seeking to solve remains unanswered."

On this assessment, it is perhaps as well that ACHCEW and Toby had made Stephen Dorrell's acquaintance several years earlier. Had they not been successful in forging a healthy relationship with him at that time, they might have got an even worse farewell from him at the end.

It was Stephen Dorrell's final point, coupled with Kenneth Clarke's observation that the precise role of CHCs was never really determined, which led me to speculate on what might have been if the founding fathers of ACHCEW had gone for the notion of a National Council rather than a confederation of member CHCs. This would probably have been accepted as the way forward by Barbara Castle and

David Owen at the time, and would have been established and functioning in that capacity by the time the 1979 government and "Patients First" came along. CHCs and their still youthful national body would probably have survived "Patients First", although it would have been easier for opponents to argue the 'potential danger of the national council adopting a role as a national political spokesman' – which plainly would raise hackles in a government containing Dr Vaughan, Mr Clarke and Mr Dorrell (not to mention Mrs Thatcher). It may well and possibly would have precipitated an earlier confrontation with ministers, making abolition a working option at any time in the 1980s and 1990s. But the existence of a national council, had it survived 1979–82, would at least have clarified the question of CHCs' ability to speak on national and health policy issues.

* * *

In every case I asked former ministers for a valedictory statement on CHCs, giving thought to issues such as the remit they were given, the appointment or election of their members and the alleged variability in performance. I was looking for an objective ministerial assessment of the real worth of the councils, given their known resource and statutory limitations. The Tory ministers of the late 1980s and 1990s and Earl Howe conveniently fall into two 'pro' and two 'anti' responses, which are summarised below:

Edwina Currie (anti): "I'm afraid I never thought CHCs were very useful and refused to serve on one in Birmingham in the 1970s. I far preferred to serve on the health authority itself, and eventually chaired it.

"The best people to represent the public are those already in post, e.g. local councillors. It was a sad day when Kenneth Clarke turfed councillors off health authorities.

"CHCs were talking shops, paid for by the taxpayer, but without the resources to undertake worthwhile research or any decision making power.

"It was never my job to hold them to account (was it anybody's?). And anyway, what could the criteria have been for 'good' or 'bad' performance?"

Edwina Currie apologised for being so negative, and accepted my thanks for her comments quite graciously. At one stage, she was Rod Griffiths' chairman on Birmingham Health Authority. Rod remembers her as keen to get things done, vivacious and sparkling. He says she showed the same characteristics in her time as a member of Birmingham City Council – and she obviously took positive memories of the council with her when she moved on to Westminster and her subsequent career.

Tom Sackville (anti): "I found them extremely varied. Some took their role as the voice of the patient very seriously, while others saw it as a way to enter politics unelected, and to express their opposition to the policies of the government of the day.

"Dealing with local authority members, I am suspicious of appointed councillors [on health bodies]. It seems as if they don't have enough to do in their own authorities...

"I think CHCs would have been better if they had been based on voluntary organisations such as the Patients' Association."[*]

---

[*] Jean Robinson, a former chair of the Patients' Association, has a diametrically opposite view. As an ACHCEW nominee to the General Medical Council, she greatly valued the constituency and the two-way communication network that her connection with CHCs provided. In conversation with me, she said that "from my point of view... there was a network you could consult, and there was a network you could feed information into, and if... it had just been the Patients' Association, it wouldn't have been the same." It

Tom Sackville gave me his mobile phone number so that I could contact him when he was out of his office. When I called him, he told me "Get off the phone quickly. It's costing you the earth." I asked him why, and he explained that he was on holiday with his family in South Africa. We agreed to speak the following week when he would be home again.

John Bowis MEP (pro): "I served on Wandsworth CHC before I was a member of parliament. I continued to keep in touch with them as local MP and later as Health Minister.

"CHCs were not perfect, and varied in procedures, impact and scope. They were useful as a forum for debate and in the supervision of the local health authority. They were most effective in providing information, advice and support for individuals with problems in the health service. They were less effective in claims to represent local communities."

In Mr Bowis's opinion, the success of the 'patient's friend' function was the achievement of the full-time staff and volunteer workers of the CHC. The council itself was effective "if it built a relationship of trust with the health service management and professionals. It proved itself if it showed it did its homework and made objective judgments." His conclusion was that in most cases the CHC was better than the alternative bodies suggested.

John Bowis had this to say on the democratic pedigree of CHCs: "A weakness was always the democratic base. It was a mixture of political and NGO nominations. Often this meant party posturing. But more often that wore itself out and a constructive creative tension earned mutual respect and effective collaborative work. Direct election would have

---

is safe also to speculate that the late Dame Elizabeth Ackroyd, herself a distinguished former chair of the PA, and Kate Patrick, in her day a CHC member, chief officer, and Director of the PA, would have been inclined to agree with Jean Robinson.

polarised [the] membership and made CHCs less objective and independent."

Earl (Frederick) Howe (pro): "At their inception, CHCs were a well-conceived innovation. Many did a first class job in representing the interests of patients and the public. Others were less successful. Inevitably however, over a period of 25 years, the context in which CHCs operated saw changes.

"CHCs need not have been abolished. Rather, they should have been improved and updated to ensure that their rights and responsibilities reflected current reality and that the performance of the best was achievable by all.

"The issue with CHCs was not the legitimacy of their members but their effectiveness. The degree of effectiveness was primarily attributable to the number and calibre of the members and staff in individual areas.

"Direct elections might have had the advantage of raising the public profile of CHCs, which in many cases was non-existent. However, I do not believe that they would necessarily have produced a more capable or committed membership. On balance I believe that direct elections would have added little value to the process in exchange for quite a lot more bureaucracy.

"Patients' Forums ought to provide a good, if rather more expensive, basis on which the interests of patients and the public can continue to be upheld and protected. The mistake the government is making with Foundation Trusts is to confuse this wider role with that of the governance of a particular NHS organisation. The roles are different."

Earl Howe extends his perspective to look a little at the future for public participation in health matters. This is not out of place, because in whatever way public representation evolves over the coming years, it will rest heavily on the experience of 1974–2003 and the imprint of community health councils will be there, whatever the effort made to suppress it.

When New Labour took power in May 1997, the first Secretary of State to be appointed was Frank Dobson. I have described Frank Dobson's attitude to CHCs in some detail elsewhere. As Secretary of State, he saw a future for CHCs, but he did sense change emerging in the philosophy of patient and public representation which could have clear implications for their future functioning. He explained this to the 1998 ACHCEW conference in Birmingham in terms of a government-stimulated shift in orientation of the NHS towards patients and their expectations. Had he remained in office as Secretary of State, he would have advanced pragmatically, looking to see where a gap or a vacuum emerged as the focus changed, and what adaptations or complementary elements in the functions of CHCs were desirable.

Frank Dobson was happy with the existing range of CHC responsibilities. The legitimacy of CHCs in the redress of grievances could have been confirmed and codified, and their representational role continued. He was quite categoric that CHCs should always have had a duty to assist NHS complainants, adding that notwithstanding the FPC regime in place in the earlier days, "even at the outset it would have been a good idea". He had examined possible alternatives and concluded that local authorities were unlikely to be the answer: "It's not been the forte of local authorities generally speaking." Even with MPs "you get a wide variation when it comes to the representation and redress of grievance function."

Mr Dobson would not have abolished community health councils peremptorily as his successor did, but he is not a member of the CHC supporters club. His pragmatic approach echoes that of earlier Labour ministers, and owes much to his roots in the centre-left of the Labour Party, his political background in Yorkshire and in London, and his personal kindliness. But even if he had remained as Secretary of State, there would have been changes in patient and public involvement, and the extent to which CHCs survived would have rested entirely on their usefulness as part of the new structure as it developed.

Towards the end of 1999, Frank Dobson resigned as Secretary of State to fight the London mayoral election for the Labour Party. He was succeeded by his former Minister of State, Alan Milburn. Alan Milburn is MP for Darlington, a seat which borders on the Prime Minister's Sedgefield constituency, and has been described as close to Tony Blair politically as well as geographically. Mr Milburn presented the NHS Plan to parliament in the summer of 2000. Work on the Plan began with the Budget in March 2000, though a number of the principles and innovations introduced must have been in existence for some time, awaiting their moment. It is not difficult to deduce from Frank Dobson's remarks about the future that he knew something about them when he was in office a year earlier.

The NHS Plan was founded on ten core principles, one of which was "The NHS will shape its services around the needs and preferences of individual patients, their families and their carers." The foreword was written by the Prime Minister himself, and contains this statement:

"We decided to make an historic commitment to a sustained increase in NHS spending... In doing so, we offered the nation and those in the NHS a deal. We would spend this money if, and only if, we also changed the chronic system failures of the NHS. Money had to be accompanied by modernisation; investment, by reform. For the first time in decades we had to stop debating resources and start debating how we used them to best effect."

Money comes with modernisation and more effective use of resources. The executive summary tells us that "For the first time, patients will have a real say in the NHS. They will have new powers and more influence over the way in which the NHS works." In his introduction, the Secretary of State said that the Plan "sets out the steps we now need to take to transform the health service so that it is redesigned around the needs of patients." No one can argue with these laudable objectives. The change of emphasis referred to by the Prime Minister could only come as an enormous relief to people who had been struggling with an increasingly restrictive financial regime since 1974. The way ahead must have looked bright and fulfilling after the interminable gloom.

For those who had been doing their best to represent the patient and public interests in the NHS, it must have seemed that the millennium really had come. But, by the time you get to page 95... "community health councils will be abolished and funding redirected to help fund the new Patient Advocate and Liaison Service and the other new citizens' empowerment mechanisms". The section containing the death sentence even begins ominously:

> "In 1974 the then government tried to give greater prominence to the views of patients by creating community health councils. They attempted to combine three distinct functions: supporting individual patients and complainants; monitoring local hospital and community (but not primary care) services; and providing a citizen's perspective on service changes. It is time to modernise, deepen and broaden the ways that patient views are represented in the NHS."

The paragraph is downbeat, hollow and negative in its intention. The use of the expression "the then government" implies "old fashioned", and the verbs "tried" and "attempted" hint at best at only partial success. No reference is made to what had been achieved by patient and public representation up to then, nor are the services of CHCs given any kind of credit. More than twenty-five years' work on the part of several thousand staff and volunteers – and with it, all the good will towards the NHS they brought with them – is dismissed without acknowledgement. When it is remembered that the abolition of community health councils was incorporated into the Plan at the last minute before publication and without any prior consultation with those affected, there is no more accurate term to describe this treatment than "shabby".

This criticism is not entirely unjustified, since Alan Milburn's name is indelibly associated with this particular section of the NHS Plan. Some people view the abolition of CHCs as a personal decision on the part of the Secretary of State; others have gone so far as to suggest some kind of vendetta. Still others have seen the sinister hand of Downing Street as the assassin and Alan Milburn as the hitman. The manner in which the decision was inserted into the Plan and conveyed to those affected, and the fact that every alternative suggested (among others by the Parliamentary Select Committee on Health and numerous Labour MPs) was rejected out of hand by the government tends to give credence to these theories. It is therefore only fair that the Secretary of State's point of view should be heard. So I asked Alan Milburn for his thoughts on CHCs as a feature of the NHS over recent years, and the reasons why he believed they had had their day. I told him that if this were too big an undertaking, a brief outline of his views would be acceptable. Mr Milburn wrote to me as follows, and as in the case of Stephen Dorrell, I have set out his answer word for word to speak for itself:

"I took the decision to abolish CHCs because I took the view that patients needed to have a voice inside the National Health Service. As you know this was the point that was made very forcibly by Professor Sir Ian Kennedy in his enquiry into the tragic events at Bristol Royal Infirmary.

"It seemed to me that CHCs had done a good job although of course, there were issues about the variability and quality. Increasingly, however, more specialised functions were needed. The role of advocacy, for example, is very different from that of immediate advice.

"I could never understand the argument of those who said that the proposal to abolish CHCs would somehow weaken patients' presence in the NHS. In fact, the reforms that I put in place – both organisationally in terms of patient forums etc., and institutionally in terms of patients being able to express a choice about where they are treated, when and by whom – represented a real strengthening of patient power in the Health Service."

I have strongly criticised Alan Milburn and his decision to abolish CHCs at several points in this book, and I still fail to understand why it was so important to him, and why the blow was delivered so brutally. Nothing I can see in his letter is sufficient to justify his summary action. Nonetheless, for the purposes of this appendix I have made up my mind to give him the last word, and to present his case without further comment.

Mr Milburn resigned as Secretary of State for Health in the summer of 2003 and was replaced by Dr John Reid. Community health councils themselves survived until the beginning of December 2003. It is interesting to note that at the time of writing, the Secretary of State is Patricia Hewitt, who in the 1970s was one of the many gifted people working in voluntary organisations and pushing forward the frontiers of social justice in this country to whom I referred in Chapter Five.

References and Bibliography

A

ACHCEW – Annual Reports 1978-2003
        Handbook for CHC Members (1994)
        The Patients' Agenda (1996)
        CHCs Making a Difference (Ben Griffith) (1997)

C

CHC Annual Reports, 1975-76 and 2000-03
CHC NEWS Archive 1975-1984
Chisholm, Malcolm, MSP – Speech to the Scottish Association of Health Councils, Perth, September 2003

D

Dabbs, Christopher – At The Crossroads, (Degree Dissertation, 1999)
Department of Health – The Role of CHCs (November 1989)
    - Code of Conduct for CHC Members, (Revised Edition, 1999)
    - The NHS Plan (July 2000)
Department of Health and Social Security – SI (1973) 2217, Regulations for Community Health Councils (December 1973)
    - Health Reorganisation Circular HRC (74)4 (January 1974)
    - Democracy in the National Health Service (May 1974)
    - Patients First – A Consultation Paper (December 1979)
    - Health Circular HC(81)15 – Establishing Circular for CHCs (December 1981)
Dorrell, Rt. Hon. Stephen, MP – Speech to ACHCEW Annual Meeting, York, July 1991

H

Hallas, Jack and Fallon, Bernadette – Mounting the Health Guard, (Nuffield Provincial Hospitals Trust, 1974)
Hallas, Jack – CHCs in Action, (NPHT, 1976)

Ham, Prof. Chris – Evaluating the Success of CHCs as an Example
of a Recent Innovation in Health Policy (SAUS, Bristol, July 1980)
Hogg, Christine – Representing the Consumer: Community Health
Councils Fifteen Years On (1989)

　　- Back From The Margins (January 1996)

　　- Papers and Project Proposals for ACHCEW, (1989-1997)
Hutton, Will – New Life for Health (Report of the ACHCEW
Commission on Public Representation, 2000)

I

Insight Management Consulting – Resourcing and Performance
Management in CHCs (The Insight Report) (November 1996)

K

Klein, Rudolf and Lewis, Janet – The Politics of Consumer
Representation (Centre for Studies in Social Policy, June 1976)

L

Levitt, Ruth – The People's Voice in the NHS (King Edward's
Hospital Fund for London, 1980)

M

Marre, Lady Mary – Community Health Councils – A Personal
View (Article in DHSS publication Health Trends, August 1975)
Marre, Lady Mary and Collis, Councillor Ken – Report of the
Ministerial Advisers on CHCs (Appendix 2) (March 1975)

N

NHS Executive – Letter (EL(92)11) to Chairmen of Regional,
District and Family Health Service Authorities (March 1992)

P

Phillips, David – Establishing CHCs (M.Phil. Dissertation, 1978)

R

Richardson, Tom – The Public Voice in the Health Services
    (Anglia and Oxford Regional Health Authority, 1995)
Robinson, Jean – A Patient Voice at the GMC (1988)

S

Smith, Martyn – Twenty Five Years with West Birmingham CHC
    (West Birmingham CHC, 2000)
South and West Association of CHCs – A Performance Evaluation
    Framework for CHCs (February 1997)
Spilsbury, David – Trumpet Voluntary (South Birmingham CHC,
    June 2003)

V

Vienonen, Dr. Mikko – CHCs and the Democratic Deficit
    (Speech to ACHCEW Annual Meeting, Eastbourne, July 1999)

W

Walsh, Peter – Cock-Up or Conspiracy? (MBA dissertation, 2002)

Glossary of Acronyms and Abbreviations

ACHCEW	Association of Community Health Councils for England and Wales (The Association of CHCs)
AHA	Area Health Authority
A&ORHA	Anglia and Oxford Regional Health Authority
AM	Assembly Member (Wales)
BASW	British Association of Social Workers
BDA	British Dental Association
BMA	British Medical Association
BMJ	British Medical Journal
CAB	Citizens' Advice Bureau
CHAI	Commission for Healthcare Audit and Inspection
CHC	Community Health Council
CHRE	Council for Healthcare Regulatory Excellence
CPPIH	Commission for Public Participation in Health
DGH	District General Hospital
DHA	District Health Authority
DHSS	Department of Health and Social Security
DMT	District Management Team
DoH	Department of Health

EL	Executive Letter
FHSA	Family Health Services Authority
FPC	Family Practitioner Committee
GMC	General Medical Council
GMSC	General Medical Services Committee (of the BMA)
GP	General Practitioner (Family Doctor)
GUM	Genito-Urinary Medicine
HC	Health Circular
HRC	Health Reorganisation Circular
ICAS	Independent Complaints Advisory Service
LHC	Local Health Council (in Scotland)
MENCAP	The National Society for Mentally Handicapped Children
MIND	The National Association for Mental Health
MSP	Member of the Scottish Parliament
NAHA	National Association of Health Authorities
NAHAT	National Association of Health Authorities and Trusts
PA	Patients' Association
PAA	Principal Administrative Assistant
PALS	Patient Advisory and Liaison Service
PCT	Primary Care Trust
PFI	Private Finance Initiative
RAWP	Resource Allocation Working Party
RCCS	Revenue Consequences of Capital Schemes
RCGP	Royal College of General Practitioners

RHA	Regional Health Authority
RHB	Regional Hospital Board (predecessor to RHA)
SAA	Senior Administrative Assistant
SDP	Social Democratic Party
SWOT	Strengths/Weaknesses/Opportunities/Threats
VAT	Value Added Tax
WHO	World Health Organisation
WI	Women's Institute
WMRHA	West Midlands Regional Health Authority
WRVS	Women's Royal Voluntary Service

Index

A

Abel-Smith, Prof. Brian, 49
Ackers, Sir James, 97, 104
Ackroyd, Dame Elizabeth, 265
Advisory Group on Alcohol (Haringey), 208
Age Concern, 216, 228
Airedale (CHC), 104
Alder Hey Hospital, 176
Alderson, Patricia, 223, 226
Alexander, Roy, 93
Alison, Michael MP, 45–46, 250, 251
All Party Parliamentary Group on CHCs, 197
Anglia and Oxford RHA, 199
Area Health Authorities (AHAs), 44, 77, 78, 80, 114, 122, 254
Arrowe Park Hospital, 138
Association of CHCs for England and Wales (ACHCEW)
- creation and early meetings of, 61-63
- standing committee and secretary/observers, 66-67
- limitations of, 107, 205-206
- special meeting, 15 February 1980, 115
- payroll and VAT status, 142
- 1984 financial crisis and committee of inquiry, 141-144, 166-167, 185, 205
- Stephen Dorrell meets standing committee, 162
- search for performance standards, 18-21, 101-103, 156-166, 170-179, 183-184
- key publications in 1990s, 193
- Core Policy Priorities, 186
- regular publications (1998), 184
- response to threat of abolition, 12, 14
- alternatives to CHCs, 194, 197, 227-232
Austin (-Walker), John MP, 31, 32, 103, 134, 140, 203

B

Barking CHC, 138
Barnby, Clive, 224, 225
Barnet AHA, 82
Barnet and Finchley CHC, 138
Barnet General Hospital, 65
BBC (radio and television), 40, 41
Bessey, Gordon CBE, 62–65, 132
Bexley CHC, 103
Birmingham Regional Hospital Board (RHB), 95–96
Black, Sir Douglas, 23
Black Report, The (Inequalities in Health), 23
Blair, Rt. Hon. Tony MP, 27, 28, 33, 35, 257, 268
Blears, Rt. Hon Hazel MP, 203
Bolter, Vera MBE, 210–211
Bottomley, Rt. Hon. Virginia MP, 167, 261
-     review of NHS complaints procedure, 167
Bowis, John MEP, 203, 250, 265
Bradford CHC, 190
Bradley, Keith (MP), 203
Bradney, Dave, 42
Brecon and Radnor CHC, 224
Brent and Harrow AHA, 129
Brent CHC, 128–133
Brent, London Borough of, 128
Bristol CHC, 138
Bristol Royal Infirmary, 176, 207, 271
British Association of Social Workers (BASW), 239
British Dental Association (BDA), 65
British Medical Association (BMA), 23, 65, 113, 115, 122,
           182, 215
BMA General Medical Services Committee (GMSC), 122
British Medical Journal (BMJ), 113, 135
Bucky, Ruth, 83, 84, 208, 209
Bury CHC, 63, 200, 201
Butler, John, 144

C

Camden and Islington AHA, 82
Camden CHC, 105, 180
Cardiff CHC, 225
Castle, Rt. Hon. Barbara MP, 47–49, 52, 62, 251, 256, 262
Casualty Watch, 51
Central Birmingham CHC, 63, 93, 133
Central Middlesex Hospital, 129, 131
CHCs
- annual reports, 55-57, 68, 80, 104, 113, 192
- establishing circulars (HRC(74)4 and HC(81)15), 61, 125, 127
- funding and budgets, 36, 38, 57, 77, 103, 107, 110, 179, 238
- CHC News, 41–42, 52–53, 58–63
- closure of CHC News, 118–120, 125–126
- reduction in numbers, 125, 137-138
- regional groups, 66, 249
- the 'variability' argument, 16, 17, 22-24, 33, 156-159, 194, 202, 254, 256, 260, 265, 272

CHC members, 17, 47, 199, 202-203, 242-244
- chairmen, 85, 89, 129, 208, 209
- RHA nominees, 88-89, 243
- local authority nominees, 130, 212, 214, 243, 256, 264-265
- voluntary sector representatives, 88, 90-91, 213, 243, 256
- relationships with staff, 58, 208-210, 214, 215

CHC secretaries/chief officers, 30, 68-72, 107, 148, 209, 210
- appointment and quality of, 47, 57-58, 68-72, 92, 106
- grading and salary scales, 57, 69, 238
- performance and contribution, 72, 129, 202-203, 226, 255

"CHCs in England", 116, 123, 126
"CHCs in Wales", 116, 123

District General Hospital (DGH) 81–82
Dobson, Rt. Hon. Frank MP, 182, 196, 228, 250–251, 267–268
Dorrell, Rt. Hon. Stephen MP
- meeting with standing committee of ACHCEW, 19
- letter EL(92)11, 162–164
Durham CHC, 70, 190

E

East Birmingham CHC, 93
East Cumbria CHC, 62
East Leicestershire CHC, 209
Edgware and Hendon CHC, 41, 138
'efficiency savings', 83
Ellam, Geoff, 105, 180–182
Enfield and Haringey AHA, 81–83
Ennals, Rt. Hon. David MP, 63, 254
Essex AHA, 82
Essex, Barrie, 98
Evans, Bill, 224

F

Fallon, Bernadette, 53
Family Health Service Authorities (FHSA), 165–166
Family Practitioner Committees (FPC), 145, 156, 201, 240–241
Finch, John (Leicester University), 133, 185
focus groups, 170
foundation hospitals, 30
Fowler, Rt. Hon. Norman MP, 125, 134, 145–146
Furr, Beryl, 30, 99, 165

G

Garner, Mavis, 203
General Medical Council (GMC)

internal market (in the NHS), 168
Islington CHC, 82, 173

J

Jenkin of Roding. Rt. Hon. Lord (Patrick), 23, 78, 113, 115,
        122, 126–128, 255–258, 260
Jenkins, Sue, 133
Joseph, Rt. Hon. Sir Keith MP, 78, 250–251, 259

K

Keegan, Kevin, 41
Kennedy, Prof. Sir Ian, 271
Kensington, Chelsea and Westminster AHA, 53, 82
Kensington, Chelsea and Westminster (North East) CHC, 53
Kensington, Chelsea and Westminster (South) CHC, 18
Kent, Gill, 42, 119
King's Fund, The (King Edward's Hospital Fund for
        London)19, 36, 42, 48, 50–54, 59–60, 70, 100, 113, 170
Klein, Prof. Rudolf, 17, 44–45, 84, 90
Knox, Julian, 204

L

Labour Party, the, 27, 132, 267–268
Lammy, David MP, 13
Lancet, The, 113
Leeds Eastern CHC, 62
Leeds Western CHC, 133
Leicestershire CHC, 137
Levitt, Ruth, 42, 53–54, 59–60, 92, 113, 220, 229
Lewis, Janet, 17, 44, 84, 90
Lewis, Rita, 165, 251
Lewisham CHC, 138
Liberal Party, the, 27, 44

M

Milton Keynes CHC, 137
Mitchell, Jeannette, 129
Moberly, Patricia, 203
modernisation (New Labour policy), 28–29
Morris, Rt. Hon Alf MP, 139
Moss, Cyril, 83
Moyle, Rt. Hon Roland MP, 250, 254–255, 258
Mullins, John, 108
Municipal Journal, 114

N

Nairne, Sir Patrick, 64
National Association of Health Authorities (NAHA), 41
National Association of Health Authorities and Trusts
        (NAHAT), 41
National Council for Civil Liberties (NCCL), 138–139
Nationalised Industry Consumer Councils, 43, 217
Newcastle-upon-Tyne CHC, 80, 209
NHS, the (National Health Service)
-       complaints procedures, 21
-       Confederation, 34
-       Dentistry, 167, 184
-       Executive, 20, 163
-       managers' attitudes to CHCs, 23, 78-79, 159, 162,
        196, 206-207
-       Ombudsman, 167
-       Providers and Purchasers, 199
-       Regional Offices, 20, 103–105, 168
-       Trusts, 189, 227–228
NHS and Community Care Act 1990, 167
NHS Plan (2000), The, 268
NHS Reorganisation Act 1973
-       Reorganisation White Paper 1972, 43
-       Reorganisation Bill 1973, 43-46
-       early stages, House of Lords, 44